Yoga, MS and Me

By

Maria Hawkes

Shield Crest

© Copyright 2013 Maria Hawkes

All rights reserved

ISBN   978-1-907629-62-4

MMXIII

Published by
ShieldCrest
Aylesbury, Buckinghamshire, HP22 5RR
England
www.shieldcrest.co.uk

Acknowledgements

With enormous thanks my husband Chris for his love and friendship and for also being my photographer.

Thanks also to my daughter Michelle and son Dominic for their help and support in creating this book.

A particular thank you to my parents, close family and dear friends for their belief in me and encouragement to write this book.

Contents

≈ 1 ≈

My youth……is this where M.S began?

Multiple Sclerosis (MS) is a neurological condition that affects the central nervous system. According to the Multiple Sclerosis website, the most common type of MS is 'Relapsing Remitting', which affects around 85 per cent of everyone diagnosed. It means that symptoms appear (Relapse) and then fade away, either partially or completely (Remitting). The 'Relapsing, Remitting' label, can help to explain MS to others and help you to find the best treatments but it cannot predict exactly how MS will affect you.

I've been pondering a lot lately about how exactly I developed Multiple Sclerosis. I was diagnosed as having this strange condition in February 2002, 11 years ago. The proper diagnosis I later received was Relapsing, Remitting Multiple Sclerosis; what did it all mean? I still felt none the wiser after receiving that news. The wording of its title meant absolutely nothing to me at all. It still all sounds rather obscure. How was I meant to understand the implications of it all?

I thought I would try and put into my own words my thoughts and feelings about this condition and how it has affected my life so much. I have spent the last 11 years trying to find various ways in which to treat the many unusual things that have happened to me and carry on living with an invisible enemy.

I've asked myself on numerous occasions; when did it all start? Was it just something I was born with or did it begin developing in my childhood? I don't have all the answers to my questions; all I do know is that there is no known cause for MS and no known cure as yet, but I still remain ever positive that somehow, somewhere, a cure will be found.

I personally believe that it may have begun developing within me as a child of eight years old. Somewhere in the confines of my memory stick the days of my youth; I am able to remember times when I was happy about life. In my family, I have a sister and brother. My sister Karen is the oldest of all three of us. My brother John is just over two years my senior. We are all so different in our own unique ways. Karen, the bubbly, outgoing one with lots of friends, was always the protective one over us both. Then there's John, the quiet but friendly lad, who you couldn't help but admire. He was such a sporty type who loved football.

They both shared a common interest; running. At every given opportunity they would both race against everything and everyone. Myself on the other hand; I used to race after them both on my bicycle. I quickly realised that this was the only way I was ever going to keep up with them both.

We are all individuals who formed a great family unit. I was a rather quiet and shy child. My friends today will all laugh at this statement because they all know me to be the opposite! I am now a chatty, outgoing person but I'd like to think a good listener too. I've always loved life and as a child I enjoyed nothing more than to go to the great outdoors with my two beloved dogs. Growing up, we were lucky enough to live beside a farmhouse so, frequently, I would venture across the adjacent fields whilst singing contentedly to myself. Maybe it was just my naivety of life that made me do this.

I remember being an eight year old girl and living life to the full. To me that meant nothing more than singing and walking. On a daily basis after school I would go to visit horses which would be grazing in nearby fields. It really didn't matter to me what the weather was like either. Even if it was sunny, rainy or blowing a complete gale, I still wanted to be outdoors. Feelings of contentment were always present inside me and I was oblivious to all negative thoughts and feelings and constantly craving happiness. Little did I know that things would change at any time.

Events shortly started to unfold which I would remember for a long time. The year was 1977; I remember the month being January because it was so close to my ninth birthday. I'd woken up late that morning for school but didn't really mind too much as I was lucky enough to live close to the school and didn't have too far to go on foot. I remember it was such a cold winter's day. There was no snow on the ground but it was still fresh and the sun was desperately trying to break through the clouds, so I walked the short distance to school, rubbing the sleep out from my eyes as I went. I'd hoped to see my friends at the school gates but suddenly realised the time and started to hurry along just before the school bell rang. All of my friends had already entered the building.

My school day began hurriedly but dragged rather slowly after that. It was amazing though how quickly I did get home afterwards. I thought to myself whilst running home, Zola Bud couldn't catch me even if she tried. She was my favourite runner at that time and someone I was told ran barefooted.

I do remember finding it so hard to concentrate on much that day because I knew we had a gymnastics competition fast approaching. I was so excited because I found something that I was passionate about and was inspired by a brilliant teacher. I'd been picked for the team previously and had been competing in local competitions. My team mates and I had been practising on the school field that day and whenever possible all my weekends were taken up with doing these strangely obscure but wonderful movements. Gymnastics seemed to be constantly on my mind.

I quickly arrived home and entered the living room to see my mother standing on a chair patiently cleaning the windows. She asked me if I'd had a good day and I replied; 'It was OK'. I watched her carefully doing such a diligent job and cleaning every single corner of those windows with such precision and pride. Within ten minutes of watching her though, I felt a sense of doom and gloom. I just couldn't understand how anybody could actually enjoy doing such a boring job.

Feeling particularly sad that the day was almost over and I hadn't done any more fun activities, I made up my mind to call on my close friend Susan. She didn't know I was planning to visit her that day and I couldn't ring her as we had no mobile phones then. At that time we didn't even have a house phone. If only we were as lucky then as we are today, maybe the event that was about to happen would have been avoided.

Susan didn't live too far away but far enough for me to want to cycle. I figured that wheels would be much quicker than using my legs. My mother, on the other hand, refused my request to go. She was adamant I should walk and not use the bike. I remember her making up some excuse about it getting dark soon.

Of course being the stubborn child I was, I ignored her plea and set off on my bike. I knew that she had gone upstairs to continue cleaning the windows and would be unaware that I had disappeared. I only wish now, in hindsight, I hadn't been quite so stubborn.

I left the house quite quickly through the back door and took my bike hurriedly from the outhouse. All the while I kept thinking I could race there and back and my mother wouldn't even notice I'd gone. How wrong I was. I grabbed the handlebars of my bike and swiftly raced up the garden path with my head down and my mind focused. I went hurriedly up the footpath and reached an opening which led up a steep hill towards Susan's house. After reaching the house, I parked the bike against a wall and I knocked on the door. Her mother opened it and told me she was out. Never mind I thought, it meant I could get home before anybody had even noticed my disappearance. I set off on my return journey and cycled to the top of the hill, I then pedalled a little further and a little racier than I normally would, racing against time. So onwards and downwards I travelled, gathering speed as I went. Halfway down the hill the strangest thing happened; I felt just like I'd fallen asleep on the bike. Everything just went completely dark and it was like someone had blocked out the sun. What was going on?

The next thing I knew was when I awoke in a strange room. There were two or three faces staring intently at me. For a moment nothing seemed to register or make any sense at all. Had I been asleep and just woken up from a dream? Was I still asleep and was this my dream? My head hurt and I felt very sick. Where was I and why were these strange faces staring intently at me? More to the point, who was I? My mind was just in a total state of confusion. How had I got here and how long had I been here? I just didn't feel right at all.

I sat up and immediately started to vomit in a bucket that happened to be at my side. My head hurt and I was trembling. I knew then that something bad had happened to me but I just didn't know what it was. As I looked ahead again, a rather shaky voiced man with kind blue eyes said to me; 'Do you know who I am? Do you remember me Maria?' I thought for a moment. Who is this person? He looked so concerned about me but I honestly did not know him. Everything felt unreal and I really did not even know my own name, let alone his.

All I guessed was that I lived here but where was here? It really was strange to be in a house I did not even recognise, with people I did not know. It was obvious that they knew me and I guessed they must be my family. I looked around the room in the hope that I would recognise something but nothing registered at all. It seemed to take a long time for my memory to come back.

When the haziness began to lift, I noticed a small, white dog. That was when my memory returned and I looked at my brother and said, 'How can I forget your ugly mug John?' Recognition sunk in and I looked up to see a very sad looking mother. I began apologising slowly for what I'd done and I can remember her words being kind and gentle as she spoke and said; 'Oh Maria, we just need to get you sorted out first and then we can talk'.

An ambulance arrived and I was taken to hospital and kept in for a whole week's observation. For some reason I just couldn't understand why I was put into a side room all on my own.

Although my head really did hurt and every time I got up from the bed I fell back down again, I started to remember exactly who I was and tried to piece together what had happened but I really couldn't remember anything about that day.

I'd never been anywhere on my own before so this was all new to me. I wasn't afraid though, just very overwhelmed by everything. All I began to think of was that I needed to get better for my birthday party, which had been organised already for the following week. I'd been so looking forward to it for months and in my adolescent way, I desperately wanted to be home for this big day. It was all I seemed to focus on because, in my family, we loved Christmas and birthdays. We'd always celebrated every single occasion and at every opportunity.

Headache or not, being an optimist, I kept leaving my room and headed down the corridor just to find a friendly face. One day, after I'd just had my head x-rayed by a friendly nurse, I walked down the corridor to find her. I could see her through a window in an office. She looked really busy and was checking out some x-ray results with a man who looked like a doctor. I heard them talking plainly through the door. What they said next has always stayed with me. The doctor told the nurse that the damage was already done and that it was over to Maria to heal herself now and that it may, or may not affect her in later years and only time would tell. I was listening quite intently when the conversation just seemed to stop. All of a sudden the nurse opened the door and looked straight at me.

'Oh Maria, how long have you been standing there?' she asked.

I remember saying quickly; 'Is that true what the doctor's just said about me?'

The nurse seemed to feign surprise and looked away from me and said; 'Come on you, you should be back in your room, not up here.'

She seemed very flustered at the time, which left me considering everything I'd just overheard. What had it all meant? I remember asking my parents later on that day what had been discovered from my x-ray results and was told that I was alright and could soon go home.

I later discovered from my sister Karen that she and a friend had witnessed what had happened to me on the day of the accident. Apparently, I was on my bike going down a hill at quite a considerable speed and at the bottom of the hill there is a barrier. I'd gone straight over it and landed upside down on my back, smacking my head on the concrete and breaking my glasses. Karen had gone to look for some help for me and had returned with a middle aged lady who had carried me home. I had been unconscious for some time.

All I knew is that it was long enough for me to feel the way I did. It felt like the longest sickness bug I'd ever experienced in my young life! I was told I'd suffered concussion and had experienced trauma from the impact of the fall. The worst part of all was the prolonged headaches that I experienced continually for months.

It isn't until now, when I'm much older and wiser, that I realise the trauma was in fact coming from my brain. It is my theory and my theory alone, that the bump to my head contributed in some way to me later developing multiple sclerosis. Whether it is in some small way or not, I just don't know because I can't prove it. There is no known medical evidence to back up my theory. Everything I've written in this book is purely based upon my life experiences.

I continued with my great love of gymnastics but did it a little more gently and not at all competitively. It seemed to be much easier and more enjoyable to do gymnastics slowly and with more breath control and I began to do a lot more stretching than I'd previously done. Little did I know how important gymnastic movements would become in later years but without the competitive element.

It took some courage but, on getting a new bike for my birthday, I got back into the saddle once again and faced my biggest challenge of all, cycling. Well, did my legs tremble that day? It was as if I'd forgotten how to ride a bike. I must have looked like a child learning to ride for the first time. After riding once more, doing gentle gymnastics and just generally taking care of myself, I realised just how important my life was.

Family life was really good and once again things seemed to progress smoothly. I hoped this was to be the end of my bad luck and life would only get better. Ever the optimist, I always thought life was for living, loving and giving and I really wanted to do all three. I honestly believe to this day that the bicycle accident, in some small way may have contributed to me later developing MS but have no proof of this. This is my own theory.

When we are young, we seem to be able to put tragic events behind us. We have a fantastic way of moving on and forgetting about the dramas in our life. So that is exactly what I did. I still visited the horses daily and walked across the fields with my dogs. Sometimes I even ventured to walk barefooted across an odd field on a hot summer's day. My memories of childhood began to improve and I wanted to find happiness once again.

Sometimes we can sit and wonder where life will take us but I believe that fate decides where and how we go.

≈ 2 ≈

From Teenager to Adult

Well, I carried on doing what children do, I began growing up. Over the next few years I progressed into a teenager and believe I was an outgoing teen and not the rebellious type. So, because of this, I started a babysitting job for a few years to earn extra money. It was an enjoyable experience to look after two young children, an older boy and younger girl. They really were well behaved for me and I was asked to sit regularly. It made me feel that one day I would like two children of my own. When I did baby sit, I found that after the children went to bed it was an ideal situation for me to do school work. I tried hard at school but was not presented with the same opportunities that children have today. For me, my priority was to get a job in order to help support my family. My father had been diagnosed with a heart condition at 32 years old and I wanted to help to ease the burden on my mother who also worked full time. Both Karen and John also worked and contributed weekly.

After leaving school I accepted a full-time position working in a toy factory. Being young, I worked very hard indeed and the factory environment meant I had to grow up fast. I was no longer the shy sixteen year old girl who had recently left school and I was gradually becoming a young woman. My outlook on life began to change too; I developed a sense of humour and appreciated being part of a team. This allowed me to join in with the group activities. It was a job that I did for money but I made a lot of good friends whilst working there. As my bank balance grew, so too did my confidence. I was now able to purchase the contact lenses that I had only ever dreamed of owning. My family were also coping much better with my weekly payments.

Things were really looking up in my life and I was feeling very happy inside. That was, until one working day, the girls suddenly started to faint on the factory floor. One by one everyone began passing out. The next thing I knew was that we were taken to hospital. It transpired that a nearby factory had been leaking chemicals which entered through our air vents. After a visit to hospital we were eventually given the all clear and sent home. None of us was able to really ascertain what happened that day. All I knew was that I began developing rings under my eyes and started feeling very lethargic. As a result I left the factory and I can only assume that this could, once again, be another contributing factor to me developing MS later in life. The nearby factory was then closed down and I set out in search of a job I felt more passionate about. Although the working atmosphere in the factory had been fantastic, I knew that it wasn't the right career path for me.

Shortly after that I found a new full time job, one better suited to my personality. It involved caring for the elderly in the community, on a 'one year' Government Training Scheme. Although I really enjoyed it, it only lasted for the year but at the end I decided that it was the right time for me to settle down with my then partner. I was given the opportunity to move in with him, which meant I would live in a different area. A new beginning in the countryside away from the village I had always known seemed daunting but rather exciting at the same time.

Picturesque views that I had only ever dreamt about became a reality. I found contentment within myself and once again, a new found confidence. It was at this time I had the chance to begin to understand myself better and to develop my interests. From this I realised that I still had a love of horses and what better place to get involved with them than where I was living. Whilst out walking my dog one day an opportunity presented itself. Knowing there were a number of stables close by, I took it upon myself to ask if I could be of assistance. I made it known that I knew very little about horses but that I was a fast learner and willing to try anything. From this, my proactive approach enabled me to set up my own business looking after horses. I learnt valuable life lessons about self-employment which, at the time, I did not realise I would use again in the future.

At the age of nineteen it felt right to get married and after two years we decided to start a family. I dreamed of still having two children of my own to complete my life and had my beautiful daughter, Michelle, first and then, nearly three years later, along came my loving son Dominic. Unfortunately, couples break up all the time and sadly that is what happened to us. The marriage fell apart and it was an irretrievable situation, which eventually led to divorce. So at the age of twenty eight I found myself alone except for my two children and a golden labrador. I wasn't afraid because I knew I could cope with whatever life put me through. I had two really good reasons to keep it together and those two reasons were my life.

My children and I pulled together through a very stressful time and I tried my best as a mother to talk to them whenever I could. I explained where daddy had gone and why. I told them we both still loved them so much but we just could not live in the same house anymore. My belief has always been the same; just because we divorced each other does not mean that we divorced the children. I always allowed their father access to see them at weekends. Obviously, stress did play a big part in my life at this point as I missed the children at weekends. Once again, I asked myself, did stress contribute in some way to my emotional state of health? Is stress a factor in me later developing MS? In my opinion it is because so much happened around this time that it may have upset my nervous system. This is just another theory of mine and one I often wonder about.

One fine day whilst out walking our labrador, Kelly, with Michelle and Dominic, I developed what can only be described as net curtains being pulled across both of my eyes. Trying not to cause alarm, I gradually turned back along the way we had been walking and slowly headed home. On my return, I turned on the television and made sure that everyone was OK and then lay down on the sofa with my eyes closed. Here I remained for almost half an hour and when I opened my eyes the haze was still there and stayed for the majority of the day. I tried not to make a fuss and just carried on trying to be the bright, breezy mum and friend for the rest of the day. I did not know then that this was known as Optical Neuritis in people with MS. This episode happened when I was twenty nine years old, fifteen years ago.

Time moved on and when both the children started school, I worked a few part-time jobs to provide for us. Food was always put on the table and nobody went hungry.

Although life was very hectic and at times stressful, I always tried to make time for fun. John, Karen and I all had a close relationship with our father whilst growing up and we would spend hours together learning various gymnastic manoeuvres from handstands to headstands. John could always walk the full length of the room on his hands and it was the headstand that I mastered. I tried to re-live this happiness with my own children, creating a warm and caring atmosphere in which they could reside. I loved the sounds of their laughter. If they were both happy, then I was too. Hoping that I could give them both love and security in their young lives was my aim and I always allowed their friends to come and play games or just watch TV. They too used to like to do gymnastics in the living room or garden. I had enjoyed it myself as a youngster so much that I understood their joy.

We were very lucky because of the amount of neighbourly support we received. Living in a close-knit community meant that close friendships were developed. In the following years, help was always available when needed. Our summertime would be spent together chatting and laughing happily. There would be regular barbecues cooked on a patch of grass in front of one neighbour's house; the same patch of grass on which everyone began doing gymnastics. Cartwheels and handstands were also performed by the children to perfection and the parents also tried providing hours of shared laughter. This really was a time of 'togetherness' with wonderful memories being made and the circle of friends we formed is still as strong today. Both my friends, named Claire, had children who would always join in with sport of any kind but especially seemed to enjoy gymnastics. Claire, Tammy, Beverley and I had water fights that somehow ended up in the house and we laughed until our ribs hurt. Our trampoline was used a lot by everyone together with the swing ball. We were a very active, lively, happy and friendly group. It was around this time that I realised how much joy everyone seemed to gain from doing gymnastics and I wondered if I would ever be able to do something similar in life to help others. It was something I began to think about seriously. Fate always does seem to play a big part in our lives and I believe what happened next was meant to be.

It was shortly after our summertime bliss and completely by chance that I found myself chatting one day to a young mum at the school gates whilst waiting for Dominic. She started talking about the weather and then about her son's temper tantrums. The next minute she began asking me if I knew anyone who might be interested in volunteering as an assistant gymnastic coach for our local area team. The classes were to be held on a Saturday morning for up to six hours. So, without hesitation, along I went the following day to the leisure centre and a week later I began my training. It was wonderful to meet up with such keen, enthusiastic girls between the ages of 5 and 15. I began to help out with warm-ups first and then learned from my instruction booklet how to plan lessons. Although I enjoyed the learning experience, I realised it was too competitive an atmosphere for me to be in. I didn't like the harsh way the coach taught the girls. It made me realise that they deserved a little more respect for their efforts as they really were trying so hard to do well in this competitive environment. I felt so sorry for them that I decided to leave this position after a few months as I no longer wanted to be working in such a bad atmosphere and I did not like the stress that came with it. I felt the coach should have been a lot more tolerant towards the students and the following year, I heard through friends that the coach had been dismissed for various reasons.

I had learned enough about the gymnastics to know the importance of a good warm-up and cool-down routine. I'd written lesson plans whilst there, not realising that this would be so relevant to me in the future but without the competitive element. I knew then that I wanted to help people of all ages do some form of gentle exercise and feel good about themselves but I was unsure what that was. I was hankering after something. In my heart I knew gymnastics was a brilliant sport but I could no longer feel good about the winners and losers in it. It was so unfair, there had to be something I could teach people that would make everyone feel equal.

After raising the children for two years on my own, I finally felt ready to move on and find further happiness. It was at this time that my present husband, Chris, came into my life. We met in the winter when I was aged almost thirty one and my life began getting even better. When I met Chris I knew that we could have a life together and we inevitably fell in love. He was very easy going and at the time, exactly the right tonic for us. Michelle and Dominic seemed to accept him as a friend fairly quickly. Suddenly, we were taken out on day trips to places we'd never been and he really made the effort to fit in with us. Love and friendship blossomed and we started to become inseparable.

After being with Chris for over a year we decided to have a family holiday in glorious, sunny Spain. It was an all inclusive holiday, kindly offered to us by Chris' parents, Pat and Graham. How could we possibly refuse? It was a fabulous week's holiday and one we will not forget. Michelle and Dominic got to experience a different culture; education and fun. Chris, being a strict vegetarian for some twenty years, tried to warn us to watch the food in the hotel. On the second to last day Graham and I made the mistake of trying some pork and on our return, at the airport, Graham suffered with severe stomach cramps, sickness and diarrhoea. By the time we had driven home I too began feeling ill. My body shook continuously and I just collapsed into a chair. I thought I had just picked up a tummy bug. My mother had awaited our return and was on hand to help. Doctors came and assumed I had contracted either e-coli or camparla bactra. Then tests came back stating it was salmonella food poisoning; most people brought presents back from Spain but I had to be different.

My friends were at the door kindly asking my mother how I was doing. Although I felt sluggish, it was still so good to know I had friends who cared. My next door neighbour, Tracy, was very good at the time. She would ask if I needed anything. Chris rang his mother that week and discovered his father had salmonella too. He was laid up in bed exactly the same as me. We both assumed it was the pork we had eaten at the hotel that was to blame.

Three months later I thought I was beginning to recover, so I decided to go jogging. Not sure where I was jogging to, I kept going at a steady pace and jogged for hours as I found the fresh air really did help me. I started to breathe deeply in and out through my nose whilst jogging and began to gaze around me at the greenery of the woods I found myself in. It helped me begin to feel so calm and peaceful, both inside and out. I had not realised then the importance of breath control. It was as if the pains inside me began easing as I let the air escape from my lungs. The feeling of going back to nature once again was the tonic I'd needed all along. I did not know that this scenario would be used in one of my 'visualisation journeys' in the future.

Before we'd gone on holiday, Chris and I had started to manage a fashion shop in town. Chris still worked full-time as he had a mortgage to pay on his own property. He did help out whenever he could but for the best part of the day I was working on my own. It was my little dream shop, I'd really put my heart and soul into the business. We had sold clothes, shoes and even hair accessories. Unfortunately, because I had no family living close at that time and I was so ill in bed, we had to give up the shop. It did break my heart to not re-new the lease on it but we had no choice.

It was after twelve weeks of carrying salmonella that problems within my body increased. I spent the next year in, what can only be described as, constant bodily pain. The pain was so severe that it reduced me to tears. What I experienced was pain, numbness, pins and needles, tingling and muscle spasms in various parts of my body. I was given so many different painkillers by my GP to try and help that I felt like a hypochondriac each time I went.

Understandably, my close friends didn't know what to do or say to make me feel better. How could they understand what I did not understand myself? However, I cared enough about them to hear about their everyday life situations; at least it helped me to block things out. Talking to others always helped me understand that I wasn't alone. Chris was so supportive at this time and called the doctor out to me at least twenty times that year. It was when my big toe on one foot began twitching I realised I had a serious problem. My doctor was actually at the house and saw this happen and she was mortified. I knew something was going on inside my body but not exactly what. It was like an alien with no name. I didn't know what was happening to me but I still wanted to remain positive as a person but found it difficult at times.

It was the morning of New Year's Day that I began to notice even more changes within my body. The previous night I'd been out with friends and had agreed to meet up with Chris just before 12 am to dance and to bring in the New Year together. I only had a couple of drinks because of the medication I was taking. We'd enjoyed being out with our friends and headed home together laughing and joking in such high spirits from our dancing. We both thought the New Year would bring a new beginning.

I awoke on that cold frosty New Year's morning, still feeling happy and exhilarated inside from the previous night's fun. I only discovered I had problems when I tried to get out of bed, my legs just didn't work. They totally gave way beneath me and I collapsed in a heap on the floor. As I tried to get up I just couldn't because my feet felt like two blocks of cement. The more I tried to get myself up the more I fell down again and I felt so exhausted trying. It was the strangest feeling ever; wanting to do something that my body just didn't want me to do. I kept on trying to pull myself up from the floor. When I decided to give up and just stay where I was, I started to laugh at myself. Through my dismay I began to think; what must I look like sitting here? I laughingly said to Chris, 'Hey darling, I think maybe we danced a little too much last night because now I can't get up off the floor.'

Chris quickly roused from his sleep and looked down at me on the floor. He immediately looked concerned, leant down and tried his best to help me. Eventually, he managed to get me up and asked if I was alright. I leaned against the wall and tried to balance myself but it was not easy trying to stand up. My feet had no feeling in them at all. Unbeknown to me, Chris had done some chiropody training previously, so he knew that numb feet meant problems. Although he did look very concerned, he managed to stay quite calm and gently got me seated on the end of the bed and left the room. Minutes later he re-appeared carrying a cup of tea, which he placed carefully on the nearby dresser. Then he asked if I had any sensation back in my feet at all. It became apparent to me then that I did not feel a thing. He quietly told me that I must pack a bag and go straight into hospital as the doctor had already been rung. I'd been so shocked by my disposition that I had not even heard Chris on the telephone.

A few hours later I found myself in Middlesbrough General Hospital where I was led into a ward by a nurse. There I underwent various tests to try to ascertain what was going on. A lumbar puncture was carried out, which involved a tube going into my spine and draining fluid from it. I then had to remain still on my side for a couple of hours. It was from this test that the doctors discovered I had inflammation in the spine. Then a nerve ending test was carried out. Whereas those test results proved to be inclusive, after having all these checks done I was sent home with more painkillers and told to rest. 'Rest I thought, how can I rest with all of this going on?' My mind and body were in turmoil.

It was after leaving the hospital and on my return home that the numbness and pins and needles in both my legs began increasing. What has brought this on I thought? All I could think of was that maybe dancing in my boots on New Year's Eve had caused the problems in my feet. I was convinced that no matter what had caused it, I would get better. Never for a minute did I doubt this or foresee any problems ahead.

Sleeping did become quite difficult. Chris showed me how it was done because he never suffered from insomnia. It became my daily routine to try to tire myself out enough to sleep at night and I walked as much as my body would allow.

Then I noticed how difficult walking became. At this point in my life I could barely walk to the local shop. Yet again my close friends helped me when needed. The more I tried to walk in a straight line, the harder it became. My legs felt as though they were no longer mine. People usually don't have to think about how they walk but I found it necessary. Passers-by looked at me sympathetically; I really didn't want to walk at all. A lot of time was spent indoors and I only ventured out when absolutely necessary.

The following year felt like a fight for survival. I joined in with the family fun as much as possible and smiled my way through the pain. It was the love of my family and friends that helped me stay strong. Although it was difficult sometimes, I tried to hide it. The daily aches and pains and loss of sensation in my limbs became so familiar to me but it was the loss of balance and walking to one side that was the worst. My mind felt strong even though my body did not. I had not yet learned that one day I would be able to help the mind and body work together as one.

I can reflect on a time one Mothering Sunday when Michelle had a friend staying overnight. Being the thoughtful child that she was, she decided to get up early and make me breakfast in bed. What a lovely idea I thought and whilst laying there I heard chattering coming from downstairs whilst the preparations were being made. The sound of laughter was audible as they crept upstairs. Suddenly, the door flew open and I heard; 'Surprise'. I faked my shock, as Michelle entered the room first, carrying a tray. I tried to raise my arms to retrieve the tray but to my dismay; my right arm had gone numb and I could only lift my left arm. Chris reacted very quickly on realising the situation and took the tray from Michelle saying; 'Oh thank you girls, what a lovely thought, I'll give it to your mum when she's woken up properly.' We both knew this was a cover-up but one which Chris knew I'd appreciate.

I did eat breakfast that morning using my left arm whilst pretending to everyone that I'd just slept on my right arm. We tried to joke about it, humour actually does always help. Not knowing why all these strange occurrences were happening was probably the most confusing part of all. How do you tell your ten year old daughter that you cannot enjoy her lovely breakfast because you cannot raise your arm to hold a spoon?

My children were always there, so supportive and giving. It was, and still is, an unconditional love. Dominic would pick me flowers from the flats where we lived. I once even received a letter from the local housing asking me if my son could please stop picking flowers, which I found quite funny because he was only young at the time. Michelle would be constantly with me in the kitchen asking to bake. We were very close.

I believe it was sometimes hard for Dominic to understand why I had to refuse to play football in the park with him; not just one day but on many days to follow. I took both my children to the beach on numerous occasions and we had spent some quality, family time together and it was so important for us to keep on doing that. Football was Dominic's life and Michelle loved the beach. How could I stop doing the things that we had always done; the fun things that families do? No, I thought; carry on trying to find the answers to your own health, be strong and brave and look ahead to a bright future. I wanted us all still to have a normal, family life.

As a child, I learned to play the piano and had loved the keys so much that I'd bought myself an organ. I fervently began to play as much music as my fingers would allow and they did sometimes ache. I played passionately but I would not give up. I believe music helped me a lot to get rid of any angry, negative emotions and no longer gave the troubles a face.

I had patiently waited for my body to heal itself but when it didn't, I could wait no longer. It was help I needed. I really did want to know what was wrong. So Chris decided to help by offering to pay for a private specialist to see me at the hospital. So we booked an appointment through the doctor the following day. It wasn't a long wait, only a matter of a few weeks. The appointment was made for me to visit a specialist, who, to my mind, would undoubtedly be able to find out what was wrong with me and cure my ailments as I still thought I had some sort of bad virus. I believed there would be a reasonable explanation for the strange happenings. There had to be somebody who could help me feel part of the human race once again and I put so much hope into my meeting at the hospital.

≈ *3* ≈

Finally given a diagnosis…. Or was I?

After arriving at the hospital on that wet and windy morning, we were led into a comfortable looking waiting room and only waited a couple of minutes before being greeted by a rather well-dressed, middle aged man in a smart suit. He seemed to be very pleasant and after only a few minutes asking questions regarding my health, we met with a rather agitated response. I could tell by the reaction he gave that here sat someone who just didn't know what was wrong with me. It was when I mentioned I'd been feeling very tired over the past year I was quickly told I had Chronic Fatigue Syndrome or ME and that I'd be alright. I heard the words 'paracetamol' and 'plenty of rest' and that was it. I no longer felt reassured that I would be given any answers about that which was going on within me.

I could tell by Chris' face that he was not too happy about what we had just heard. Almost immediately he responded by stating flatly that it was something else. He knew I had not been right for quite some time and felt this was a mis-diagnosis. He was a little annoyed and I think everyone present could see that from his facial expressions. I can honestly say he loved me and the fact that he had paid for me to be seen by a specialist who didn't seem to care was not the issue; it was the way in which he had spoken to me.

We were quite quickly ushered out of the room and told another client was expected at any time. Chris made a point of saying, 'Well that was a complete waste of one hundred pounds.' He was absolutely mortified that I'd been told nothing helpful. I knew I felt tired but I really didn't believe this to be the right diagnosis for me at all. Did he think I was imagining the pain?

Something deep inside kept nagging me and telling me something important had been overlooked. I tried not to dwell on it too much but knew I needed an answer to my questions. How and when could these answers ever be found I thought?

So I carried on with my day to day life as normally as possible realising how much I valued the love and support of my fiancé, Chris, and my family and friends. I was lucky enough to have friends who helped me so much just by being there. Their support was wonderful. When a night out together was arranged, my whole group of friends would come. Their friendship and care meant so much to me through this difficult phase in my life and without it I would have been quite lost and alone.

I found joy listening to the sounds of laughter between my children. Fun and laughter always brought me back to reality. Chris would take Michelle, Dominic and me out whenever there was an opportunity. He would just happily say, 'Come on then you lot, get ready because we're going out somewhere'.

One sunny day he took us to a place with a fantastic play park. After entering the grounds, both Michelle and Dominic ran straight to the climbing frame and I happily joined in with their fun. We must have been there for a full day because I noticed it was beginning to get dark and suggested it was time to leave. We gathered up the coats and set off back to the car. On leaving the play park I noticed the main entrance gate was closed which meant we couldn't leave so Chris, being his usual laid-back self, looked at us and said; 'Oh well, it looks like we're stuck here for the night'. I just looked at him and laughed. Luckily the caretaker spotted us and unlocked the gate.

At least for a while my mind had been taken away from my mis-diagnosis and I did my normal daily chores that came with family life. I always made sure both Michelle and Dominic were taken to and brought back from school every day by myself or Chris. As soon as they went to school my day's work would begin. I still did a few cleaning jobs and worked as hard as my body would allow.

When I Was Given The Right Diagnosis

It took two M.R.I scans and another year of me harassing the doctors for them to discover I had not gone mad, nor was I a complete hypochondriac but that I had a genuine reason for all my complaints. The first M.R.I scan had shown some lesions (scars) in the brain but not conclusive enough to give it a name. So I waited again for a few more months and was then referred to a different hospital for a follow-up M.R.I scan. It was this second scan which had my doctor looking at me sadly as she delivered the news. I didn't know that this news would change my life forever.

The year was 2002 and I remember it very clearly. An early morning call from the doctor's surgery asked me to go straight to my own doctor. I knew immediately something was wrong and guessed that something had shown up on my scan. In the waiting room that morning it felt like the longest day of my life. What could it be I thought? Understandably, all sorts of things were going through my mind that morning. I wondered if it was a brain tumour or had I had a stroke but my optimism replaced it with; whatever it is I will fight it! I knew that hospitals were marvellous places so I thought whatever it was it could be treated.

When I did see my doctor she kindly invited me in but with a grave face. I sat down in front of her and was already prepared for the worst possible news. I anxiously waited for the results to be given and my heart was in my mouth. The doctor just looked at me sadly and started apologising. She said 'I'm so sorry Maria but you have Multiple Sclerosis. I really believed you didn't have it'.

My first thought was what is that? In all fairness, I didn't have a clue. I'd heard of people having this strange illness but I didn't actually know what it was. Then I realised there seemed a lot more to it because the first word was 'multiple'. How could there only be one problem when it seemed like a lot more?

After being told the news, the doctor looked quite sad when she next spoke to me. I think only because she'd seen me a lot during that year. She explained a bit about the disease itself but I just could not comprehend it all properly. How could I possibly understand what I'd just been told? Only the words; 'disease of the central nervous system' seemed to stick in my mind. I wondered what that actually meant and if there was anybody out there who knew about the disease itself. I was told that I would be referred to a neurologist who may be able to help me understand a little more and maybe slow down progress of the disease. I left the doctor's room feeling shocked and confused. Then the feeling of knowing that, at last, I had a name for this alien inside my body made me feel calmer. At least now I knew I hadn't been going mad all this time. Where do I go from here? Do I go back to a cold, lonely house or do I go and look for a friendly face?

I felt really lost and bemused that day so the last thing I wanted to do was to go home to the cold, empty house. 'My friends are all busy working,' I thought, 'and my family lives too far away'. Who do I turn to for support? I wondered. Now, I wasn't a woman who had ever depended on anyone, I was someone who could be depended upon. Anything I could do to help my friends and family I'd always done and it was this independent nature which moulded me into the person I am. I'd tried never to burden friends with my problems but coped with whatever came my way. It seemed strange to me to stand outside the doctor's surgery that day wondering where to turn. I suppose everybody must feel the same way when being given news that shocks you to the core.

After staring into space for, what seemed like, an eternity, I wandered aimlessly from the doctor's surgery towards the main road, whilst feeling a mixture of sadness and relief. The sadness, due to the fact I had a disease of the central nervous system that I didn't know anything about and relief that something had shown up on the M.R.I scan to say I was completely sane and not at all crazy.

I crossed the busy main road in a bit of a daze and walked slowly up the street. I thought at least people would understand a little more why I was walking slowly. I didn't want to be pitied, just to be understood. It just felt like some days the world had quickened up and I had slowed down. So I figured I now had a name for it and could at least try and understand why this happened in the first place. Not knowing then that I would spend the next few years of my life still trying to figure it out.

So, that day, I carried on wandering towards the local duck pond. I began gazing into the water where I obviously thought I would find all the answers to my problems. It seemed strange to me how everyone else around me just carried on with their normal daily activities and I couldn't understand why their lives were so unaffected by all of this upset in my life. It wasn't until much later on that I realised life carries on for everyone else no matter what one's own circumstances are. How could their lives possibly be affected by mine? I couldn't change my situation and I would not have wanted to upset their lives. Life owed me nothing and I needed to face facts. I had a problem, which was mine and mine alone but I so wanted to offload the burden to someone else.

The first person I actually did see that day was my good friend Claire. She happened to be in the right place at the right time. Her youngest daughter was with her in a pushchair. We began talking, mainly about the family, because Claire has four girls. Eventually, I nervously broached the subject of the diagnosis I had been given. Remaining quite calm and in control, Claire actually helped me that day by rationalising what I told her. She managed to laugh with me that I'd not been going crazy after all. I told her I finally had a name for my strange behaviour. It was wonderful to have such a good listening ear as Claire's that day. The disease did not seem quite so vicious after our little chat.

It was from that moment on and thanks to my fantastic friend, I decided multiple sclerosis would not beat me. My mind was made up, no matter of what this disease tried to rob me; I would fight it all the way. Somewhere from the depths of within, I found the strength.

Of course I had to firstly inform my family of my prognosis. I rang Chris and waited for his shocked reply. He then told me he would come and see me as soon as possible. Then my parents were told in as calm a voice as I could muster, only to then, understandably, be asked a huge barrage of questions. I quickly hung up and left them to inform the rest of the family. Talking about it meant I was airing the problem.

The tears began to come when I was alone and then came the anger. Deep down, I realise now, I was grieving inside for the person I used to be and being re-introduced to the new Maria. Who was she, I thought? I must try and find out. I didn't want to change because, after all, I liked the person I was and had always been happy in myself. For two years of my life I'd discovered an independence I never knew before. Although I was living on my own and raising my two children, I'd never felt alone. I'd spent those years happily bringing up my courageous children. I had worked hard and we'd pulled closely together before I met Chris.

The job of telling Michelle and Dominic had to be the hardest and most painful thing I'd ever done. Telling an 11 year old girl and an 8 year old boy that mum had a disease which she didn't really understand was not an easy task. They had always been my strength and my life and I had always tried to protect them as only a mother knows. So I sat them both down and told them as gently as possible what I had been told. I laughed about the reasons why I walked a bit funny sometimes. Dominic wondered if I could still let his friend Robert come for tea sometimes. I then hugged them both and said 'How lucky I was to have them.'

I believed they would be scared sometimes and unsure of changes they could see happening to me so I wanted to make sure I had the answers to their questions. I needed to know more so I could learn about my capabilities. I figured the more I knew the less worried they would be. It just became common knowledge in our family that mum was having an off day because MS was letting her know it was there.

≈ 4 ≈

My Visit to see the Neurologist

My doctor referred me to a neurologist at Middlesbrough General Hospital. Within a couple of weeks I had an appointment to see him at the Neuroscience's Department. So, once again, Chris booked a day's holiday to accompany me there. We entered the department and were greeted by a friendly looking receptionist who asked us to take a seat in a small corridor and told us the neurologist would see me shortly. After waiting just a couple of minutes a nurse called us in. I joked to her about me looking drunk on the way into the room because I almost tripped over her on the way. She just laughed along with me and said it was alright, and I immediately felt at ease.

We entered this small but accommodating room together and approached a man with a smile on his face. He leaned down to shake our hands before asking us both politely to take a seat. From then on, I just knew this wasn't going to be a wasted journey. I got the feeling from his friendly greeting that this man could help me and I instinctively knew I was in the right place and help was at hand and it felt so good to know this.

We sat down and waited patiently before he began asking me how I was feeling after the news that I had MS. My reaction was immediate; I said I didn't feel too good about being told I had something I didn't understand and asked if it would be possible to explain in more detail what it was. From our conversation that followed, I gathered I had, what was termed, 'Relapsing, Remitting Multiple Sclerosis' and that it was a chronic disease of the central nervous system. Basically, what this meant was that sometimes I would be ill and enter a relapsed state and at other times I would become fairly well and go into a stage known as 'remittance', when my body would slowly begin to recover.

Gradually I began to understand how the disease had been so hard to detect because it had not begun with optical neuritis, which made it difficult to diagnose. Optical neuritis meant that the peripheral vision in my eyes would be affected but not the frontal vision. However, when I thought about it afterwards, I realised my eyesight had been damaged already on the day I walked the dog with Michelle and Dominic.

All I really wanted to know was what caused it and when it would go away. It was explained to me that there were no known causes of multiple sclerosis and no known cure, at that time. I knew then that it was nothing at all like a common cold but something I would have to learn to live and deal with over the years and that there would be good and bad days ahead. Once I was told a little more about what was going on with the disease itself and the prognosis, I had a better understanding of it.

Chris remained very quiet and deep in thought whilst sitting there. Anyone who knew my husband knew him to be a quiet man but I knew him well enough to know when he's building up to say something important and this was one of those moments. He asked the neurologist if there were any treatments available to slow down the disease. He told us there were various treatments on the NHS known to be effective. Beta-Interferon injections were used to slow down the disease progression by up to two thirds and he suggested it could be something for me to consider should the relapses become more frequent. I knew it could be an option and needles never scared me. I was also told that after a relapse further treatment, comprising a 5-day course of Methyleprednisolone steroids, could be given if needed to speed up the healing process.

On my first visit to hospital that day, I was examined thoroughly and told that my arms and legs were still very strong and that I was still in good physical shape. I was then in the 'remittance' stage, which meant I was recovering, and I felt so much better knowing that people knew exactly what I was going through each time I felt pain. It was explained to me that it was coming from the central nervous system and that the MS I had was highly active; relapsing and remitting.

≈ 5 ≈

How I found Hatha Yoga and became a Teacher

My journey of self-discovery began in the local library. I'd gone there with the intention of finding answers to help me deal with MS. I have always been a huge fan of books and I'd dedicated my free time to reading all my life. I knew that if I ever had a problem the answers would always be found on the pages of a book so I spent a long time researching as much as I possibly could about possible treatments for MS. I'd read every single book the library had to offer and it really was an educational time for me.

It was completely by accident that I found a book in the health section on Hatha Yoga. I was actually looking for a book about human anatomy at the time and this book was beside it on the same shelf with a brightly coloured cover. I picked it up and started to turn the pages slowly and was amazed to see a model within the first few pages of the book looking relaxed and happy. She was seated in a cross-legged position appearing to be comfortable and on the next page was in a position that looked very similar to a gymnastic pose. She wasn't a famous model but someone who seemed to know what she was doing. That was it for me; I was completely hooked and liked the idea of trying out these wonderful positions. I thought if she can sit like a rubber man on a hilltop then so can I, so I took the book home on loan and started practising the poses.

It was amazing how good I felt even after doing the basic warm up. When I started doing the stretches I could actually feel the aches and pains inside my body miraculously alleviate. I had quite a few laughs to begin with while practising what I saw in the book. The poses didn't look easy to try at first but I found that by breathing in and out through the nose as instructed, I would be able to bend further forward. I continued practising lots of stretches and postures as shown and couldn't believe the changes within me! My tight, painful feet seemed to ease once again and my whole body seemed to change overnight. It was so enjoyable that I devoured every single Hatha Yoga book I could find.

I relished the idea of finding new challenges and realised I didn't have to use force to go into a posture but could go into it gently. Although yoga was similar to gymnastics I'd learned as a child, there was no competitive element in it at all. Sleep came so easily after years of depravation and it was such a pleasure to go to bed at night. There were to be no more pain-filled nights ahead.

After practising yoga at home alone for a couple of months, I found a couple of good Hatha Yoga classes and started learning everything I possibly could from the teachers. Whilst there, I devoured everything I was taught on the subject as I was so hungry for knowledge. It was while on the yoga mat that my knowledge of the subject was beginning to develop. It gave me a sense of feeling completely grounded. All my bodily aches and pains just seemed to evaporate. What I learned from the books and classes really gave me the strength and confidence to believe in myself once again. Finally, I really began to like who I was as a person, both inside and out, and just knew I could leave the world and all its troubles behind. I probably have more Hatha Yoga books now than the local yoga store itself! My belief has always been the same; in order for people to learn from me I need to know what I am talking about. I knew then that I wanted to teach other people about this amazing exercise.

The next thing I did was to learn as much as possible about Hatha Yoga and advanced further into BSY home study courses. I'd learnt basic yoga principles over two years from both BSY and BWY teachers and spent the following year learning everything I possibly could about postures, breath control and meditation. My first BWY teacher was a doctor's wife, by the name of Louise and she too has MS. Her patience was unbelievable and I found her lessons so relaxing and educational. I then studied human anatomy and physiology to learn more about the human body. It took me two years of study and exams to realise I was on my way to something wonderful. Gaining knowledge about this form of exercise and the philosophy involved was amazing and learning it was something I found very enjoyable. I knew I wanted to take it one step further.

All I dreamt of doing in 2003 was teach. It was forever on my mind to find a specific venue and I searched endlessly for a quiet room; one free from distractions. When I finally found the perfect place I was ecstatic as I was now able to make my dream of helping other people come true. If I could make others feel as good as I did, both inside and out, that would be reward enough. I knew I didn't want anyone else to feel as ill as I once did.

It finally happened; the big day arrived when I could actually teach. It was February, 2003 when I began teaching for the first time. Michelle had helped me with advertising by making a magnificent poster. Copies were printed and we placed them all around town. I also printed some medical questionnaires and found there was a lot of interest in yoga. After doing all of this the time finally arrived.

It was seven o'clock in the evening and I decided to teach the students once a week for one and a quarter hours. This was long enough to do fifteen minutes warm up, the postures and then a good cool down. I opened my mouth to speak and to my dismay nothing came out and it took me a good couple of minutes to actually find my voice again. Once I got over the shock of the silence, I began to speak calmly and it was then I realised this was something I had waited a long time to do.

When I began teaching, I started doing what felt so right in my heart. My love of yoga was finally being shared with people of all ages as I had a mixed age group of absolute beginners. There were some eighteen year old teenagers, a few middle aged ladies and even a seventy four year old gentleman turned up. There were about fourteen students on my very first day's teaching, which was a day I will never forget and is etched permanently in my mind. It was the beginning of being able to share my knowledge of Hatha Yoga with these keen students.

Although that first day was quite nerve racking, it was also very rewarding. These enthusiastic people had turned up and had lain on my yoga mats ready for me to teach them everything I knew. It was the best feeling I could have ever wished for as I felt as if I'd been lost and found all at once and I felt a sense of belonging almost immediately. That night the students laughed so much at the obscure positions in which they found themselves. The atmosphere was so good I felt as if life could get no better than this and my nerves disappeared completely.

I continued happily teaching these enthusiastic students, who were eager to learn as much as they possibly could. Everyone seemed to have such fun and relax totally by the end of each session. The following week, after asking the students if anyone had ached the day after the yoga session, I was very happy when everyone said 'no'. My teaching had taught me that it was very important to try and relax every muscle by the end of each session so the following day the body wouldn't ache.

I knew how important it was to give my whole attention to the students in the room so, when I entered, my mind was always on them. My own problems were left outside the room and I continued to teach happily for as long as possible without my MS bothering me much at all. I enjoyed the positive feedback I gained from the students themselves; after all, I thought, how could I become a better teacher if I didn't listen? Who better to ask than the students themselves? Listening to their comments about having a good night's sleep and feeling better about themselves was reward enough for me. I was told by various students how strong their bodies were feeling and it felt so familiar to me and warmed my heart to hear.

I took notice of their details in the medical questionnaires, which I'd asked all the students to fill in before starting. That way I knew what physical problems each had and where they were located in their body so I could modify the poses to suit each student's needs. For example, if someone had a neck problem, I would tell them to be careful not to fling their neck back in a certain pose. It was a wonderful feeling to watch the students come into a room looking tense and unhappy and then see them leave looking so much happier and relaxed.

I could see each week how they did the poses with such care and knew I was helping to do some good in the community. At last I'd achieved my dream of becoming a yoga teacher and it wasn't about my status but about doing some good to these yoga enthusiasts. It was a feeling of pure joy to prepare the room for each yoga night with my very good friend Tina who also did yoga after helping me with the preparations. Teaching was all I wanted to do and I felt I had finally found my vocation in life.

As the student's knowledge grew, so too did my confidence. At the time I'd hidden the words MS deep inside me and just tried to forget its very existence and while I was busy I forgot about my enemy. It was a big shock when, only three months later, I developed optical neuritis in my left eye and found I just couldn't see at all. It happened one morning, on a day like any other day; I woke early that morning to do a lesson plan for the evening's class only to find, to my dismay, that as I opened my eyes the vision in my left eye seemed distorted and objects were missing from my field of vision. I tried hard to focus my eyes. What was going on I wondered? I really had absolutely no idea. Then Chris insisted I went to the doctor that day and she examined me carefully doing strange tests. I had to watch her pen move from left to right and up and down but it was difficult to even see the pen let alone watch it move. The doctor then looked at me rather sympathetically and informed me that she thought I had optical neuritis and that it looked like my peripheral vision may have gone.

Although my neurologist had mentioned this to me before, I didn't really know what it meant. Did it mean that I was completely blind? All it felt like was that I was swimming under the sea. My arm had also decided to go numb in sympathy with the eye as the feeling in it had completely gone. What did I do to cause this I wondered? Then it dawned on me, I had a recent water infection and been treated with antibiotics but still felt a little under the weather. At least I knew then what the cause of the relapse was, so now it was up to me to try and get better. The worst part was that it meant I'd have to cancel my yoga class. I didn't want to but knew I would need some time to recover and go into remission.

Once again, I was off to an all too familiar place, hospital, where I was given another MRI scan. Naturally, at this point I was a bit scared. The scan picked up that the peripheral vision had gone altogether and it was explained to me that this meant I was actually losing sight fully in my left eye. I was then informed by the ophthalmologist that the optical nerve behind the eye was so damaged that with an optical torch it looked completely white inside. What could be done? I was told that my neurologist wanted me to be given methylprednisolone intravenously in a single high dose for five consecutive days. The ophthalmologist then informed me it was to help speed up the relapse I was in and send me into remission quicker. This sounded plausible and I could either sit at home doing nothing, except wallow in self-pity, or I could do something positive to help myself recover and go into remission. I chose the latter as I was not a sad and lonely person who felt sorry for herself. Although my world was an extremely distorted place, I still wanted to live in it. As long as I had yoga in my life, I could recover.

I felt even more optimistic after I began to do the alternate nostril breathing I'd learned whilst studying yoga. I knew then, alongside the help from my neurologist and my new friend yoga, I would heal and go into remission quicker. I tried to remain as relaxed as I possibly could even though I knew I had to return to hospital for five consecutive days to be given the necessary treatment. My world would not be overshadowed by this problem because I just wouldn't let it destroy me. I wanted to carry on and deal with whatever life threw at me so I could recover to the best of my ability. It was all about finding some inner strength and remembering it would not last forever and that I was just in relapse. I remembered relapses were something from which I could recover. I needed to come back as quickly as possible from the problems my body was now giving me.

My family needed me and I wanted them to see me coping well under pressure so I needed to fight this invisible enemy. I felt I was prepared to deal with the alien living inside my body simply by using everything I'd learned over the years. I knew yoga would help to align my spine and make life a little easier for me to move. There were also a lot of manoeuvres I found whilst on the yoga mat which helped to strengthen my whole body.

I underwent the treatment at hospital for five days as the neurologist had requested and actually found it wasn't so bad at all because I got to meet other people who had different reasons for being there. Some people had MS but others didn't, so I found it reassuring to know that I wasn't alone at that time and it helped having people around me who actually understood the disease. It was inspiring to see how people come together in the face of adversity. The strongest people I have ever met in life are those who have undergone treatment in hospital.

Taking the Methylprednisolone didn't bother me too much and I kept thinking it would help put me into remission quicker. I did find it gave me a horrible taste of iron in the back of my throat but on the second day I took a packet of mints along. I kept thinking of my family and how I looked forward to spending time with them at home.

Another thing that always kept me going was the thought that I would soon be back teaching again. After a couple of week's treatment I was referred back to the hospital to see how it had gone. The ophthalmologist then examined my eyes and did various tests and I was told nothing at all could be done for me now as I had complete loss of sight in my left eye. It just didn't sink in immediately but when it did, I thought to myself, maybe he's wrong; I just know my yoga is going to help me as I knew enough breathing techniques and meditation to help. So then I replied; 'miracles can happen you know'. I just knew in my heart that this was the time to practise everything I'd learned about yoga.

When I left hospital after speaking to the specialist again, I'd already decided that I would do as many breathing and twisting exercises as I possibly could. I started first thing in the morning doing deep breathing exercises to relax both my mind and body and then I did a full hour's session. I found the series of breathing exercises that helped me most were 'Salute to the Sun'. I believe to this day that it was this series of twelve breathing exercises, which I did repeatedly every day, that helped me with the improvement in my vision.

I continued with yoga at home every day as, whenever I used it, it seemed to really help and contribute to my feeling good, both inside and out. Gradually, over the following weeks I could feel my vision slowly getting better. I did eye exercises which I'd discovered from books years previously. I could then gradually make out colours that I'd once lost and then shapes returned to view. It was still dark in my eye but better than having no vision at all and I began feeling a lot more evenly balanced.

I returned to the hospital again after three weeks treatment. The usual eye examinations were carried out and to my joy the ophthalmologist told me that the left eye was showing some signs of improvement. He was quite shocked as he'd told me the Methylprednisolone would not be able to bring back my sight because the damage had already been done. Although I did feel so much stronger with help from Methylprednisolone, I believe the extra help came from practising yoga continuously both morning and night.

Whilst doing deep breathing exercises combined with meditation, I felt I was repairing the damaged nerves inside my body. I have no evidence to back up my claim but this is my own self-belief. It seemed as though the more stretching and relaxing I did the better I began to feel. It was obvious to me I just needed to keep on believing and practise what I had found.

I continued trying to help myself to the point of becoming relapse free. It became apparent that the way I dealt with stress had such a big impact on MS itself. I realised then, that I would be able to manage my symptoms much better if I did yoga every day and kept my stress levels down to a minimum. At least I was starting to understand a little more about what I could and couldn't do. It was just about me learning to accept and adjust to the changes taking place within my body.

I still kept up one-to-one teaching with my family and friends at home. Michelle and Dominic were both so flexible and a great pleasure to teach. They were both going through their own stresses at the time with exams nearing and yoga helped them both sleep at night. I found it a great joy when a friend approached me with similar problems to myself and asked if I could draw her up a lesson plan. Sharon had already been a student of mine and understood the Asana's but not exactly when to do them. She wanted to try and do the lesson plans herself and I kept in touch via mobile phone to monitor how she was doing.

I began to do more lesson plans and had the idea that just because I wasn't teaching in a venue did not mean I couldn't teach students lesson plans. It was such an incredible feeling being able to still get the yoga message across but in a different way.

I continued practising day and night whenever I could and began to find out about local MS clubs and I went to some group meetings. I joined Buddies group based in Scarborough where people with MS met once a month to chat. We all understood each other and although everyone with MS doesn't feel the same at the same time, we all have similar symptoms. Most of us understood about numbness, pins and needles and pain. It was then that I felt I wanted to do something to help these people too, people with whom I had so much in common. So I did a little bit of seated yoga with a few people and it felt so right.

I knew then that I was still on my path of learning and it was good to expand my knowledge about 'Chair Yoga' so much more. As I became more advanced with the poses at home, I decided to do an advanced yoga teaching course as I felt ready for it. Although I was not teaching **a** class of students regularly, I just knew I would do it again one day so I carried on with my learning skills until the time was right for me to teach a room full of students.

That time actually came sooner than I expected and I began searching round my hometown to see if I could find a suitable venue. Once again, with Michelle's help, I placed posters in the library and various other places and she was so helpful driving around with me everywhere. It took a while to find the right room but once I did, it was perfect.

I had been away from teaching a full class of students for some time and wasn't sure how they'd react but, to my joy, it felt as though I'd never been away. Some of my previous students returned and, once again, I had a class full of enthusiastic people. I was thrilled with the room choice; it was warm, carpeted, comfortable and very cosy. My mother helped me throughout my years of teaching and always remained steadfast on the door helping people settle in and marking them off the register while taking their payments. It was an ideal situation that really suited us both and it worked. We were a good team together and I think everyone associated my mother with comfort because she always made them feel so welcome. My parents did eventually move into the area to be nearer. I now knew that whenever I was relapse free I would be able to teach, whether it be in a venue or via lesson plans and that made me feel happier.

I do know that infections seem to pose a massive problem for me, as no doubt it does for other MS sufferers. It is only because we have reduced immune systems that we find it difficult to fight infections easily. I therefore decided that I would watch my daily diet. It was quite funny though because I love to make soups of all different kinds and I became a bit of a soup freak at this time. I started making everything from vegetable and onion, to pea and mint soups and my family knew me then as the soup lady. I believed that medicinally these soups could only help make me feel better.

What works for me might not always work for others but it did help me with my practise because it was so light on the stomach. It actually left me with enough space inside to bring in lots of air when doing my breathing techniques. I did try a spell without making soup but missed them so much I just had to carry on making them again. In fact I almost joined the helpers in the soup kitchens. My favourite soup had to be carrot and coriander and I believed that whatever was in the carrots helped with my vision. Two hours after eating my soup I would lie down on my yoga mat and practice so many different postures.

The following year, in 2004, my fiancé, Chris, and I decided to get married and buy a house. It is said that the most stressful things in life are to move house, get married, change jobs and pack for a holiday! Well two out of four of these were pretty stressful I can tell you as I concentrated all my energy on these important things. A new house brought new challenges along with it.

I had such high hopes for a good future with my family. Michelle was my oldest child at 14 and Dominic was now 11. We were all looking forward to the new move and I just couldn't wait to decorate the house but first we had to practically fully renovate it as it needed a lot of work, including double glazing and the heating needed to be sorted out. The street we moved into was only two streets away from our previous house but it was in a quiet cul-de-sac where our lives became very peaceful indeed.

This meant I could practice my yoga and it was ideal when everyone went out as it gave me more time to myself to learn about the various breathing techniques I'd read about. By putting everything into practice I felt more able to teach it. The only thing I found different about the new home was that I'd always been used to having friends call round and adjusting to life in a street where everyone was so busy was quite difficult at first. However, I gradually got used to it but think Michelle and Dominic also found it strange. Like me, they thought it was odd not having a neighbour knock on the door and call in for a cuppa and a chat. The neighbours I did see were all pleasant enough and made us feel welcome but I never intruded on their privacy as I thought they had their own lives to live and may have their own personal problems to deal with.

Life became very quiet indeed as we all settled down to our own daily routines of work and school. I knew Dominic missed having somewhere to kick his football because he'd always had an area at the front of the house to play. He was only 11 and obviously still needed to do what he was good at. Michelle, on the other hand, liked the garden that we left behind as the new garden was very small with overgrown trees. There was no privacy at the back at all as my father, being dad, ripped out every single tree in a few hours and I couldn't believe what he had done.

I seemed to spend quite a lot of time preparing work for my classes once a week and decided the time was right to do more than one class. I had endless visualisation journeys typed up which I wanted to share with my students so the time felt right to do two classes a week.

For a short while I had a beginner's class as well as some students who had been attending for years. This worked out for a while but there just weren't enough spare days at the venue. It was such a busy place with different classes all week and I found it difficult to teach my second class of students in a quiet room because, all of a sudden, loud music and banging would come from downstairs. I tried to gently turn up the yoga music to drown the noises from below but, to my dismay, it was impossible for the students to relax and the more I tried to bring calm into the room the more tired I felt.

Time progressed and before I knew it I'd been teaching for five years. I had time off for holidays and important functions but generally speaking I felt reasonably well for an MS sufferer and I was infection free. It was so enjoyable to do what always felt so right and natural and to realise I was coping quite well with the help of my family and friends. Sometimes my feet were heavy and I would fall down and occasionally this stopped me from teaching but I would always try not to let my students down and would relax at home before teaching. I had reflexology treatment every month by a really well trained therapist and it really helped alongside the meditation I practised.

Michelle and Dominic seemed to be around more to help with shopping and other chores and when they both turned 17 they passed their driving tests and had a car each so I felt very lucky as they taxied me around. I knew they were growing into two responsible adults and their help and support was wonderful.

I'd managed all this time to stay relapse free and happy but still a little guarded against my invisible enemy. I did have reminders of MS in my feet but I knew in my mind that yoga always helped me come back from any relapse and that I must not overdo things. MS is something which is always unpredictable and over which I have no control. I have tried to stop its progression with the help of yoga but I would sometimes become a little too comfortable and not prepared for anything to go wrong. Occasionally, I do ask myself why this disease would come along when least expected and it would often strike first thing in the morning on rising.

Everything was going smoothly in my life until a few years ago when in May of that year I awoke to find myself unable to get out of bed. My shoulders were very numb and I knew then I must go to the doctor. To be honest I was in shock. So with my mother's help I went along, once again, to be admitted to hospital. However, I needed my own surroundings because it was the only place I felt comfortable so I signed myself out of hospital and rang Chris to come and collect me.

After returning home to recuperate, I again concentrated on practising my yoga daily and decided to write this book to help others understand a little more about MS and how it affects people living and dealing with it. I know there are millions of people in the world with the disease and hope the tools I try to provide through Hatha Yoga might, in some small way, help other people cope better with life's many problems.

Having this condition doesn't only affect the life of the MS sufferer but also the lives of loved ones. Nearest and dearest feel so useless because they want to help so much but don't know how and immediate family and friends are afraid to say the wrong things for fear of upsetting. So please try and remember that people with MS also want and need to cope.

I've tried to show some of the postures I've done myself with the students over the years. Although it seems as if there are thousands of them, there aren't really. I will probably spend a lifetime looking for them and I hope you all understand that every single posture can be modified to suit your own needs. The postures can be done seated where necessary and furniture can be used to hold on to in standing poses.

Hatha Yoga will always remain in my head and heart and stay ever present with me as my lifelong friend and I hope you can reach out and grasp a little bit of comfort from the many gifts it brings.

What I learnt about Hatha Yoga?

Before becoming a Hatha Yoga teacher, I wanted to learn as much as I possibly could about this branch of eastern philosophy. I believed it would make me a more approachable teacher for the students. So I spent the next two years studying and in fact did learn many great things of interest; namely the fact that yoga itself has been around in some form or another for thousands of years. It is believed that the ancient sages, or rishis, practised yoga in order to help them attain enlightenment. Although the name 'yoga' is well known, it still seems to be a great mystery to we westerners as to exactly what it is. The word 'yoga' means 'yoke' or 'union'. It is about joining together the right and left hemispheres of the body as one.

The word 'Hatha' is split into two syllables. The first syllable 'Ha' means 'Sun' and the second 'Tha' means 'Moon'. What this means is, that the two words are opposite to each other, like 'day' and 'night'. 'Hatha' in Sanskrit also means 'Forceful'. Although the Asanas are forms of exercise for the mind, they are very strengthening for the body too. It does not mean that force is used to carry out the postures as this is not the case. It means the poses are held with some strength so, invariably, your body will also become much stronger in the process.

Although the exact origins of yoga are still somewhat vague, I learned through BSY and BWY teachers previously, that Hatha Yoga is the main branch of yoga, from which other branches stem. There are 8 limbs that make up this main branch and they are known as; Asana (steady pose), Pranayama (control of vital energy), Dharana (concentration), Dhyana (meditation), Yamas (restraints), Niyamas (observances), Pratahara (withdrawal of sense from objects) and Samadhi (super-conscious state).

Yoga is not a religion but more a science or art form. I was taught that due to the age of yoga and its use in ancient civilisations, the science of yoga has remained largely unchanged while humanity has continued to evolve. As I read in 'The Key Muscles Of Hatha Yoga' written by Ray Long, Patanjali, the patron saint of yoga, said that mastery combines a balance of science and art. Knowledge of science is like the colours on an artist's palette – the greater the knowledge, the more colours available. The body is the canvas and the Asanas are the pictures we create. The Asanas are mastered first in order to connect both body and mind which, in turn, initiates the path from physical to spiritual awareness. The Asanas and Pranayama (breath control) will strengthen both the body and mind. The Asana's consist of seated, standing, forward, backward and sideways bends, inversions and spinal twists.

Many people think yoga is just a series of physical postures that enable undisturbed meditation but it is so much more than an exercise class. Once the postures are mastered, various different breathing techniques are introduced, such as abdominal breathing, full yogic breath and alternate nostril breathing and much more. Then Dharana (inner concentration) starts to become apparent.

Meditation or Dhyana is usually followed last. In order to practise this, space needs to be found somewhere in the home, preferably free from mental stimuli and the room should be warm so the temperature does not distract you. Meditation, I learnt, is similar to sleep in the way that you can slip in and out of this state. No one teaches you how to sleep and, in the same way, meditation cannot be taught. However, there are skills and exercises that can help you to reach a state of meditation and it is these techniques that I used as a yoga teacher to help the students. I believe that the mind needs to be calm in order to carry out day to day activities and meditation is basically about finding quiet time. Obstacles may need to be overcome before starting this, such as anger, doubt, hatred, muscle pain, joint pain and ones ego.

Yoga really is a way of life to a lot of people and I know it has become a best friend to many and we are all on the same learning path. Whether yoga is practised on the yoga mat, in the chair, or even on a bed, it really doesn't matter as long as it is done slowly and carefully at all times. If using a chair, make sure it is sturdy when leaning on it.

It is about being in the moment, living in the here and now and eventually putting all negative thoughts to rest. Try and concentrate on the body being like a temple and worship it. This is your time, time for you to look after yourself. You are important because when you are calm and happy, so too are those who you meet.

What is it good for?

Yoga should help to:

- Relax the mind
- Improve posture
- Promote physical strength
- Increase muscle tone
- Stimulate the function of internal organs
- Promote the feelings of well-being.
- Improve flexibility

Yoga may help to cope with:

- Multiple Sclerosis
- Diabetes
- High blood pressure
- Anxiety
- Stress
- Sleep disorders
- Heart conditions

The list is endless.

It is a practice that can be carried out by people of all age groups, from the very young to the elderly. I have seen children practising yoga as young as 4 years old and as old as 84. There is no age limit at all. What is needed is breath in your body, if you can breathe, then you can do Hatha Yoga.

I discovered that by practising Asana's each morning and night, doing the various breathing techniques daily and meditating, I feel so much better inside following a relapse. I learned 11 years ago that Hatha Yoga became a wonderful tool to help me cope with MS and I hope it will help many others too.

How is it practised?

Yoga should be practised on an empty stomach; usually 2 - 3 hours after a light meal. Water should be drunk beforehand and not while practising; the reason being that while the internal organs are warming up inside the body, they are generally being massaged. If water is drunk, it may put out the furnace and the work could be un-done.

Comfortable clothing is recommended to help move around easily and I wore jogging bottoms, t-shirt and cardigan when I first started. It is a good idea to practise at home as it is both educational and fun. It is enjoyable trying to figure out why your body won't do what it is meant to do. I kept laughing at myself at first and then began self-practising with a good yoga book by my side and went to yoga classes for two consecutive years. It's always a good idea to make sure the room itself is going to be free from distractions. You could close the curtains or blinds and it might be helpful to make a point of telling your friends and family that you will be busy. It is important to establish a relaxed and tranquil atmosphere for yourself; after all, this is your time and you are very important.

Once the room is quiet, warm and airy and you have a yoga mat and a little space, you can begin your session. A good fifteen minute warm-up is recommended to start with so the body is fully prepared for the Asanas ahead. Gentle yoga music can be played in the background if preferred and a long burning candle may be placed somewhere safely nearby. It is advisable to have either a cardigan or a blanket to enable you to cover up at the end of your session because, as your body relaxes, its temperature usually drops.

It is each person's own choice as to whether or not a teacher is present to begin with. Once you begin learning, it is advisable to practise as safely as possible so having a trained teacher present is always a good idea. Take heed of your body because you are important and if anything hurts or a muscle pulls, stop immediately and start the posture again slowly.

When a posture is carried out by bending forwards it is always followed simultaneously by bending backwards or sideways to equalise the body. To begin, an inhalation is done slowly through the nose and followed by an exhalation deeply also through the nose unless doing an inverted posture and then it is out through the mouth.

Every teacher will have their own style of teaching and they will know the way that suits them best. I believe in doing a good 15 minute warm up to start the session which enables the muscles, tendons and ligaments to be gently stretched before beginning a full yoga session. When the body is warmed up you can begin a gentle routine of postures. Don't do too many if you are new to yoga and always listen to your body and how it feels in each posture. Be aware of the muscles and their purpose.

Abdominal breathing may be introduced as you progress from seated postures to following the lesson plans step by step and moving on to standing balances before slowly introducing 'Salute To The Sun'. Nothing should be hurried in yoga. Consider how you breathe in through your nose and out deeply through your nose.

After the postures have been completed the body needs to be cooled down. A 15 minute cool down session is what I always recommend. Lay down in Savasana and relax at the end of the session. This is where I usually do a visualisation journey, which enables the mind to take you away from the everyday problems of life. You may want to listen to a CD of gentle yoga music and imagine you are in your favourite place. I have written a section on visualisation journeys in Chapter 12.

≈ 6 ≈

Some Asanas I have Taught

Ihave tried to give some of the Asanas their Sanskrit names wherever possible. Some teachings differ from others so they might have different names but they are correct to that particular branch of Yoga.

Seated Postures

The main Asana in which to start the seated poses is known as 'Staff Pose' or 'Dandasana'. This involves beginning with a really good straight spine with the hands placed on the backs of the thighs to straighten the spine.

Seated Forward Bend – Paschimottanasana

1) Sit with a good straight spine.

2) Raise the arms upwards with fingers facing forwards.

3) Breathe in and bend forward from the hips.

4) Run the hands down the legs as you exhale

5) Reach for the feet and clasp them if possible.

6) Aim to bring the chest down toward the knees and breathe normally for up to 8 counts.

Benefits:

1) The blood flows to the head, the body temperature begins to drop and the blood pressure lowers.

2) This is a really good posture for insomniacs.

3) Stretches and lengthens the hamstrings and calf muscles.

4) Flexibility is improved.

!! Don't overstretch the hamstrings!!

Wide Legged Seated Forward Bend

1) Begin with a good straight spine.

2) Bring the legs apart to wherever feels comfortable for you.

3) Raise the arms straight up and relax the shoulders.

4) Inhale and then bend slowly from the hips and run the hands down the legs.

5) Exhale as you relax down towards the floor and hold it here for a couple of counts.

Benefits:

1) The hamstrings and calf muscles are lengthened and stretched.

2) Helps tighten and tone the quadriceps.

3) The chest airways are opened.

4) Very good for opening tight hips.

5) Reduces blood pressure.

6) Body temperature is reduced as the blood flows to the head.

7) Fantastic for aligning the spinal column.

   !! Make sure your spine is straight on bending forwards from the hips!!

Heron – Krauncasana

1) Bend the left leg up and place foot under right thigh.

2) Position both hands underneath the right foot. Inhale as the right leg is bent up and then lifted.

3) Exhale as the leg is straightened.

4) Eventually, try to bring the shin in towards the forehead.

5) Hold this position for a couple of counts.

6) Relax and then repeat the same on the other side.

Benefits:

1) Both the hamstring and the shin muscles are being lengthened.

2) The spine is being strengthened, whilst the nervous system is being calmed.

3) The abdominal muscles may get tightened and the digestive system gets massaged.

!! Careful not to overstretch the hamstring muscles on the back of the leg too much!!

The Inclined Plane- Vasisthasana

1) Begin with legs in front of you and arms shoulder distance apart.

2) Hands are facing backwards with the fingers widespread.

3) Gently rise upwards from the hips and try to straighten the legs.

4) If you can, you could tilt your neck back slightly.

5) Hold it here for up to 8 counts.

6) Relax back down to the floor.

Benefits:

1) Strengthens the shoulders, arms, wrists and hands.

2) Stretches and lengthens the hamstrings, shins, feet and ankles.

3) Tightens and tones the quadriceps.

4) Opens the chest airways making breathing easier for people with asthma.

5) Stimulates the spinal muscles and elongates the neck.

6) Tightens and tones the abdominal muscles.

!! Be very careful not to fling the head back to quickly!!

The Table

1) Begin with the arms shoulder distance apart, fingers widespread and hands facing either forwards or backwards.

2) Legs are hip distance apart, with feet flat.

3) Rise upwards from the centre and just breathe normally.

4) Tilt the neck back gently.

5) Hold the pose here for a couple of counts.

Rock The Baby

1) Bend the left leg and curl the foot up underneath the right thigh.

2) Place the right foot into the crook of the elbow (or wherever is comfortable).

3) The right arm is brought around the right leg and the left hand is clasped.

4) The aim is to rock the right leg gently from side to side like a baby.

5) Bring the leg down to the floor after a couple of rocks.

6) Repeat the same with the left leg.

Benefits:

1) Wonderful as a hip opener.

2) Good for strengthening the knees.

3) Stretches the hamstrings and tones the quadriceps.

4) This improves flexibility within the joints.

5) The spine is aligned and strengthened too.

6) Tendons within the groin are being massaged.

!!Try not to force the foot into the crook of the elbow.
Place it where it feels comfortable!!

Cowface – Gomukhasana

1) Start seated with a good straight spine.

2) This pose is about stacking one leg on top of the other.

3) The left leg is tucked underneath the right.

4) Bring the right leg over the left.

5) Next, try and reach your left arm up behind the middle of your back and try and clasp the right hand.

6) Be patient with yourself in this pose as it may take a while to clasp both hands together.

Benefits:

1) This is a wonderful pose for opening the hips.

2) Strengthening the arms and legs.

3) Tightening the gluteus maximus and the abdominal muscles.

4) It may also lower blood pressure.

!! Be careful not to force yourself into this posture!!

Cobblers - Bhada Konasana

1) Begin from a seated position.

2) Bend your knees and bring the feet up towards your hands.

3) Gently reach for your shins.

4) Inhale and bend forward from the hips.

5) Exhale into the bend and then relax down.

6) Come as close to the feet as is comfortable.

7) Try placing your forehead onto them in time.

8) Relax here for a couple of counts.

Benefits:

1) Wonderful for opening the hips.

2) Really beneficial to the inner thighs.

3) Tightens and tones the buttocks and legs.

4) The mind relaxes as blood flows into the head.

!!Be careful not to overstretch forwards!!

Half Lotus – Ardha Padamasana

1) Begin with a good straight spine.

2) Sit with the knees bent.

3) Gently bring the right foot up, place it on the left thigh.

4) Remain here for a few counts to begin with and then relax.

5) Place your hands, palms up, on the knees.

Benefits:

This is comfortable for meditating and opens the hips ready for full lotus.

Advanced Pose - Full Lotus – Padmasana

1) Begin with a good straight spine.

2) Place the right foot on the left thigh.

3) Place the left foot onto the right thigh.

4) Remain here for a couple of counts and then relax.

Benefits:

1) Buttocks tighten and tone.

2) Legs and knees strengthen.

3) It helps to keep the legs still if you want to meditate in this position.

!! Be very careful and warm up fully before attempting!!

Pose From Knees To Back

Hero Pose- Supta Virasana

1) Start the pose with your knees apart and your bottom on the floor.

2) The aim is to gradually bring the shins outwards and the knees inwards.

3) Just breathe away normally in this position for a few minutes.

4) To go back into reclining hero you need to first rest back onto your elbows.

5) Very slowly and carefully bring your back down towards the floor.

6) Bring your arms down slowly to rest on your feet.

7) Hold this for a couple of counts and then carefully rise up to rest on your elbows.

8) To come out of this pose, the weight is transferred forwards onto the elbows.

9) Always come up onto the knees very carefully.

Benefits:

1) Increases hip and spinal flexibility.

2) Tightens and tones buttocks.

3) Strengthens knees and legs.

!! Be very careful not to raise the knees off the floor when trying to recline downwards!!

Boat - Navasana

1) Begin seated and clasp the backs of the thighs as the knees are raised.

2) Try to find the sitting bones in your buttocks.

3) Inhale as you try and balance.

4) Exhale as you raise both arms and legs together.

Benefits:

1) One of the best poses for strengthening and toning the abdominal organs.

2) Works the muscles of the lower back.

!!Lower back slightly if any cramp is experienced in thighs!!

Childs Pose-Balasana

This is the main resting pose when doing Asana on your stomach or knees. If you have trouble with your knees, feet or ankles and feel more comfortable rising up a little, then come up to rest with your chin in your hands and rest your elbows on the floor. It can be uncomfortable to sit like this sometimes, so just try and modify this position to suit your needs. Always listen to your own body because you are important.

1) Kneel down, with your bottom resting on your feet.

2) Relax forward and bring your arms around your head or rest with your chin in your hands whichever feels the most comfortable.

3) Remain here for a couple of counts between each pose.

4) By remaining in this position for a few counts, it gives the blood pressure time to regulate itself.

Poses On Your Stomach -Bow-Dhanurasana

1) Begin by lying down on your stomach.

2) Bring your legs together, place arms by your side with palms facing upwards.

3) Rest your chin on the ground.

4) Reach behind for your feet.

5) You may find you can't quite reach them, so just hold onto your shins.

6) Breathe in and raise your head and chest up off the floor.

7) Hold the posture for a few counts.

8) Exhale as you lower back down to the floor.

Benefits:

1) Excellent for people with asthma as this opens the chest airways.

2) Good for strengthening the arms and legs.

3) Improves spinal flexibility.

4) Tones abdominal muscles.

!! Don't put too much pressure onto the feet!!

Upwards Facing Dog- Urdhva Mukha Svanasana

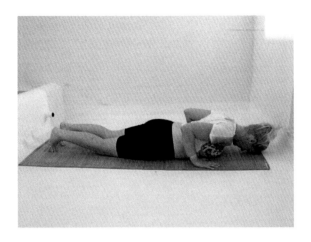

1) Lie down on your stomach.

2) Place your arms shoulder distance apart with hands forward.

3) Keep legs together with your toes tucked under.

4) Inhale before you rise up.

5) Exhale as you come up.

6) Breathe normally.

7) Hold this for a couple of counts to start with.

Benefits:

1) Good for arms and legs.

2) Opens the chest airways and helps asthmatics.

3) Helps strengthen the spine.

4) Strengthens the wrists and shoulders.

5) Works the entire spine.

!! Don't put too much pressure on your arms!!

Lunge

1) Begin with arms slightly further apart than shoulder distance.

2) Legs together.

3) Inhale as hips rise upwards.

4) Exhale as you keep the right leg back and come forward with the left.

5) Repeat the same procedure the other way round.

Benefits:

1) Stretches the thigh muscles and opens out the groin, allowing fresh blood to come into these areas.

Locust- Salabhasana

1) Begin by lying down on your stomach.

2) Bring your legs together and place arms by your side with palms facing upwards.

3) Place chin on the ground.

4) Inhale and raise the head and chest up.

5) Bring the arms and legs up and backwards.

6) Exhale as you hold the pose for a few counts.

7) Gently release and then relax back down to the centre.

Benefits:

1) Helps to improve spinal flexibility.

2) Strengthens arms and legs.

3) Tightens the abdominal muscles.

4) Good for asthmatics.

!! Be careful not to raise the neck too high in case you strain it!!

Cobra – Bhujangasana

1) Lie down on your stomach to begin with.

2) Bring your arms down by your sides with palms upwards.

3) Legs are close together.

4) The arms are bent and shoulder distance apart with the hands facing forwards and fingers widespread.

5) Inhale as you brush the nose and chin off the floor.

6) Exhale after coming up with the elbows bent.

7) Remain here for a couple of counts

8) Bring your face forward and tilt the neck only if you feel comfortable.

Benefits:

1) Opens the chest airways and may help asthmatics.

2) Improves spinal flexibility.

3) Strengthens neck, arms, legs and feet.

!! Be very careful not to overstretch the neck and hamstrings in the back of the leg!!

Inverted Pose

Shoulderstand-Sarvangasana

1) Begin by raising up both legs.

2) Place your hands on hips.

3) Gently roll slightly back and bring your hips into your hands.

4) Try and straighten your legs.

5) Keep the chin tucked into the chest.

6) Now rest the weight onto your shoulders.

7) Only hold this for a few counts until you progress.

8) Bend and part your legs as you very carefully come out of this pose.

!! It's advisable to avoid this pose when menstruating and if you have high blood pressure!!

Inverted Pose

Plough – Halasana

1) Start by raising both legs together.
2) Place both hands on your hips.
3) Gently roll back slightly onto your hands.

4) Lift the hips off the floor.
5) Go over, as in half shoulder stand.
6) Bring your legs down to the floor behind you.
7) Remain here for a few counts.

8) Relax and release after a few counts.
9) Gently bend your knees and separate them to come out of pose.

Inverted pose

Half Shoulderstand

1) Lie on your back to begin.

2) Raise your legs together straight up in the air.

3) Place your hands on your hips.

4) Just like doing a backward roll, gently flip your legs up over your head.

5) Bring the shins toward the forehead.

6) Relax in this position for up to 8 counts.

7) If you can, try to bring your hands onto your shins and rest here.

Benefits:

1) It stimulates the nervous system and relaxes the whole body in the process.

2) May strengthen the spine.

3) Good being in this position after a hard day's work. It's otherwise known as the pose of tranquillity.

Asanas laid down

Corpse-Savasana

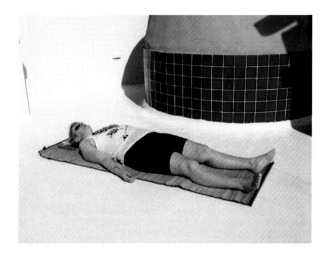

1) Begin by lying down on the floor.

2) Stretch out the legs.

3) The spine is extended and the sacrum is flat on the floor.

4) Allow yourself a chance to relax.

5) Tuck the chin in towards the throat so the neck is stretched.

6) If you have a back problem, bend the knees up.

7) Do the same as above and relax.

Benefits:

1) Lying down on the floor with your eyes closed will allow you to completely relax.

2) Although this pose is surprisingly more difficult than it looks, with practice the mind and body will become calm.

Thread The Needle

1) Lie flat on your back with your knees bent.

2) Place your right foot on your left thigh.

3) Inhale as you raise your head slightly and thread your right arm through the hole that has been created.

4) Exhale as the left hand overlaps the right.

5) Hold the pose for a couple of counts and hug the knees.

6) Release and relax down to the floor.

7) Repeat the same on the other side.

Benefits:

1) Fantastic for energising the nervous system.

2) Stretches the spinal column and helps it become more flexible.

3) Elongates and strengthens the neck and shoulders.

4) Tightens and tones the legs and buttocks.

Spinal Roll

This is a spinal massage for your lower back and is carried out in between back postures to relax the muscles in the lumbar region. I always recommended students do this even when practising alone.

1) Start on your back with knees bent.

2) Bring knees together.

3) Place your hands around your knees.

4) Gently roll to the right slightly then back to the centre.

5) Then roll to the left a little and back to the centre.

6) Repeat a couple of times.

7) Place the feet back down and relax.

Benefits:

1) This can ease back pain in people with lower back problems.

2) Very relaxing between postures and may help prevent muscle stiffness.

Fish – Matsyasana

1) Begin with your legs together.

2) Place your hands on the backs of your thighs.

3) Rest back onto your elbows.

4) Inhale and gently open your chest, as you lean back and exhale.

5) Hold this for a few counts and then lean forward.

6) Transfer the weight onto the elbows to come out of pose.

7) Relax back into Savasana.

Benefits:

1) Good for asthma sufferers.

2) Fantastic for spine, shoulders and neck.

!! Be very careful not to hold the neck back if you suffer from an injury!!

Postures On The Knees

Cat – Biralasana

1) Begin with your knees hip distance apart and your hands shoulder distance apart.

2) Hands are flat and facing forwards with fingers widespread.

3) Breathe in and carefully arch your back and look upwards.

4) Hold this for a couple of counts and exhale.

5) As you exhale arch your shoulders upwards gently and bring your head down towards your chest.

6) Arch your back gently back again and relax.

!! The movement of bending your spine one way and then the other should always be done slowly and carefully!!

Downward Facing Dog – Adho Mukha Svanasana

1) Begin with your arms shoulder distance apart and hands facing forwards with fingers widespread.

2) Legs are hip distance apart, with the feet as near to the floor as possible.

3) Breathe normally and then raise the hips upwards.

4) Try and hold the position for a couple of counts.

5) Continue breathing normally.

6) Gently bend your knees down to come out of the pose.

!! Be very careful when rising upwards not to push down too hard on the feet!!

<u>The Gate-Parighasana</u>

1) Begin on your knees with the left knee pointing forward.

2) Bring the right leg out straight to one side with the foot flat.

3) Raise the left arm.

4) Relax the right arm down the leg and curl up the left hand.

5) Inhale and lean slightly over to your right.

6) Exhale and then breathe normally for a few counts.

7) Hold the position while you feel the oblique muscles being stretched gently.

8) Come back slowly to the centre and repeat the same on the other side.

The Hare or Rabbit-Sasankasana

1) Begin on your knees.

2) Place your forehead on the floor.

3) Reach backwards and try to clasp your feet if you can.

4) Bring your forehead as near as possible to your knees.

5) Next come up onto your tiptoes with your feet.

6) Gently try and go from your forehead to the crown of your head.

7) Hold this position for a couple of counts.

8) Release and relax back down.

Benefits:

1) Stretches the head, neck and shoulders.

2) Good for the spine.

3) Tones the thighs.

!! If your knees hurt in this position, rest on a towel or cushion!!

<u>Advanced Backbend</u>

<u>The Camel – Ustrasana</u>

1) Start with the knees hip distance apart.

2) Lean slightly back and place the hands on the back of the thighs.

3) Breathe normally as you reach back for your shins.

4) Try reaching back with one arm at a time to begin with.

5) When you progress in this posture you may be able to reach for the heels.

6) As this is a very intense and advanced back bend, only go to where it feels comfortable for you.

7) Stay in the position for only a couple of seconds until you advance.

!! Be very careful not to lean back too far. If it feels uncomfortable don't go backwards at all!!

Standing Postures

Mountain Pose – Tadasana

This is where all the standing postures begin. The Mountain-Tadasana, represents strength and height. It's what we climb to reach our goals. The ancient sages studied many objects and animals and stated Tadasana, or Mountain Pose, was the mainstay position.

Many people with MS have problems within the feet and legs, so this can sometimes pose a problem and I know what this feels like. It's alright to lean against a wall for support or bring legs further apart but you need to feel as grounded as possible in order to do this. I spread my legs a little more because it is more comfortable. The toes are spread wide and the feet connected to the ground with arms relaxed by your side. Try also to relax the shoulders. I try to think of the foot as a triangle and concentrate on my big toe, little toe and my heel which balances me. This helps a little with our mobility problems. My feet have been made of concrete for over 11 years now so if I can practise trying to stand and balance then I'm sure you can too. Use whatever apparatus you need to make you feel comfortable while standing.

Chair-Utkatasana

1) Stand with your feet slightly apart and arms down by your sides.

2) Take a few deep breaths in and out and then relax.

3) Raise the arms to shoulder height and relax the shoulders slightly.

4) Slowly begin bending down as though sitting on a chair.

5) Stay in this position for no more than 8 counts to begin with.

6) Then slowly rise back to the centre again.

Benefits:

1) This is a brilliant pose for strengthening the quadriceps at the front of the upper thighs.

2) It tightens the buttocks and tones the waist.

3) The shins and feet also gain a great deal of benefit here.

!!Be careful not to lean too far forward!!

Tree – Vrkasana

1) Start in Mountain Pose.

2) Shift your body weight onto the right leg.

3) Raise the arms and try to balance if you can.

4) To modify this pose, hold onto something nearby, such as a tree, wall or even a steady chair.

5) Try to focus your mind ahead onto something to balance you.

6) Hold on to something for support if you want to for a few counts.

7) Repeat the same again with the left leg.

Warrior – Virabhadrasana

1) To begin, you should step forward with your right foot facing ahead.

2) The left foot is then at a ninety degree angle behind.

3) The legs slightly apart at a comfortable distance.

4) Raise the arms to shoulder height.

5) Go forward gently and hold the pose for a couple of counts and then release back to the centre.

6) Repeat with the left leg.

7) On returning back to the centre, raise the right arm while breathing in and look at the crook of the elbow.

8) Exhale as you return to the centre again.

9) Repeat on the left side by bringing in the right foot and turning out the left.

Eagle – Garudhasana

1) Start in Mountain pose with legs at hip distance apart.

2) Arms by your side.

3) Focus on the feet being grounded.

4) Cross the right arm over in front of the left.

5) Aim to try and clasp the left hand but don't force it.

6) Cross the right leg over the left.

7) Eventually the foot will come round to the back of the shin.

Benefits:

1) Wonderful for both the arms and legs.

2) May help improve inner concentration.

3) Good for tightening buttock muscles too.

!! Be careful not to push too hard with this one!!

Forward Bend-Uttanasana

1) Begin in Mountain Pose.

2) Keeping shoulders relaxed.

3) Raise the arms with palms facing forward.

4) Inhale.

5) Exhale as you slowly bend forward.

6) Breathe normally for a few counts.

7) Bend your knees slightly if it is uncomfortable.

8) Come to a standing position slowly.

Benefits:

1) Your heart is rested.

2) The head receives a fresh supply of oxygen-rich blood.

!! Only go as far as is comfortable!!

Backward Bend

1) Stand in Mountain Pose to begin.

2) Relax your shoulders down.

3) Raise up your arms with palms facing forwards and inhale.

4) Exhale through the mouth as you gently tilt the head back slightly.

5) Hold it here for a couple of counts.

6) Bring the head gently forward again.

7) Relax and then drop the arms.

Benefits:

1) Strengthens the head, neck and shoulders.

2) Also good for the spine.

!! Be careful not to fling back your neck!!

Spinal Twists

These Asanas may help you understand the importance of a healthy spine and inner body. When the twists are done, the pelvic and abdominal organs are squeezed and flushed with blood; the suppleness of the diaphragm is improved and spinal, hip and groin disorders are relieved. Energy levels are increased as the flow of blood is improved so it can also calm the nervous system.

Spinal Twist- Matsyendrasana

1) Begin with the right knee bent over the left.

2) Place your left hand below your left leg.

3) Your right hand is behind your back.

4) Inhale through the nose.

5) Exhale as you twist your body round to look over the right shoulder.

6) Breathe normally for a few counts.

7) Come back to the centre.

8) Repeat the same with the right arm and left leg.

!! Be very careful not to twist round too far!!

Simple Spinal Twist

Easy Twist

1) Begin with a good straight spine in Staff Pose.

2) Bend your right knee up and place your left elbow on it.

3) You right hand is resting on the floor behind.

4) Inhale and twist round to look over your right shoulder.

5) Exhale as you twist round.

6) Breathe normally for a couple of counts.

7) Come back to the front once again.

8) Relax and then repeat the same on the opposite side.

Spinal Twist - Maricyasana

1) Begin by bending the right knee up.

2) Lean forward slightly and bring the right arm in towards the right knee.

3) Inhale as you try and bring the right arm inwards around the knee.

4) Exhale as you twist your right arm round your back towards the left hand.

5) Try and clasp both hands.

6) Don't worry if your hands don't meet, just keep practising carefully.

7) Release and relax.

8) Repeat on the other side by bringing your right knee up and twisting your left arm round to meet your right hand.

!! Be careful of your shoulders. Shake them out after the pose!!

Inverted Postures

Shortly after teaching yoga I began to realise that a lot of people were afraid to go into inverted postures because they involve the head being down and the legs being up (understandably so). I understood their fears but always tried to reassure them their blood vessels would not burst and they would come to no harm. Consideration was always made to those with high blood pressure or menstruating at which time it isn't advisable to do the full shoulder stand.

References were made in the third chapter of 'Yoga Pradipika' by Yogi Svatmamara relating to inversions being avoided whilst menstruating because they could interrupt the menstrual flow. Only when the menstrual flow exceeds its normal duration could it be helped by strengthening the uterine system.

The inversions are said to be relaxing and reduce stress and strain and it is always a good thing to do a few inversions if time is not found to do a full yoga session. The blood circulation to the brain is improved, therefore, so too does intelligence.

Some Inversions:	Benefits:
• Shoulderstand-Sarvangasana	Thyroid and Parathyroid by increasing blood flow
• Plough-Halasana	Helps adrenal glands
• Headstand-Sirasana	Blood goes to the brain and helps you relax

Foot Stretches

I have always found it helps make my feet a bit stronger by doing these foot exercises each morning and night. Although feet are a main concern of mine, I thought I would show you what I learned a long time ago to help ease the stiffness.

1) Place feet flat and curl toes upwards.

2) Hold for up to 8 counts then relax.

1) Have feet flat to start with.

2) Curl toes gently underneath.

3) Hold for up to 8 counts.

4) Relax toes again.

Seated Warm Up Routine

Arms

Shoulder Shrugs

Neck Rolls

Aeroplane

Prayer Poses

Spinal Twists

Rainbow Stretches

Cool down

Savasana

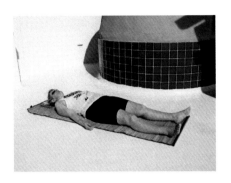

1) Relax down at the end of your session.
2) Remain here for a few minutes.

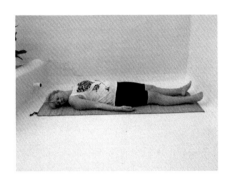

3) Gently roll your neck to the right, back to the centre and then to the left.

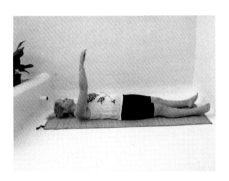

4) Inhale and slowly raise the right arm and bring it to the floor behind.
5) Flex up the right foot too.
6) Exhale whilst lowering the arm.

7) Inhale and repeat the same as above on the left side.

8) Inhale as your raise the arms over the head.

9) Rest for a few seconds and then exhale as you lower the arms back down to your sides.

10) Squeeze the thigh muscles gently together.

11) Hold them for 8 counts.

12) And relax.

13) Squeeze your buttocks gently together for 8 counts and then release.

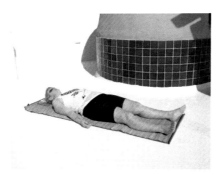

14) Relax into Savasana and try and let the mind and body settle down.

15) If any stray thoughts come into your mind, just let them go.

16) Try to imagine you are lying down in your favourite place.

17) Try to envisage it in your mind's eye, which is between your eyebrows.

Lesson Plan

1) <u>The Bridge- Setu-Bhandasana</u>

<u>Spinal Roll</u>

2) <u>Half Shoulderstand</u>

<u>Spinal Roll</u>

Seated Poses

3) <u>The Table</u>

4) <u>The Heron</u>

5) <u>Inclined Plane</u>

6) <u>Seated Forward Bend- Paschimottanasana</u>

7) <u>Rock The Baby</u>

<u>Go onto your stomach</u>

8) <u>Cobra- Buhjangasana</u>

<u>Child's Pose</u>

Kneel Down

9)   The Cat

10)   The Gate

11)   Downward Facing Dog

Child's Pose

12)   <u>Standing Forward Bend- Ustrasana</u>

13)   <u>Standing Backward Bend</u>

<u>Seated</u>

14)   <u>Cobblers Pose- Bhada Konasana</u>

Lay down in Savasana at the end.

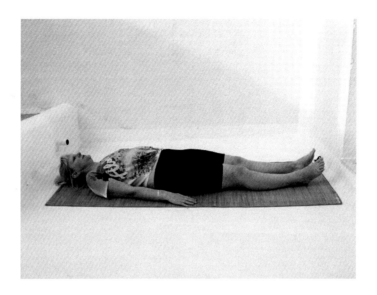

When you are ready, a cool down should be done at the end of your session. This is very similar to the warm up except your thigh muscles, buttocks and hands are squeezed together individually and held for up to 8 counts then released.

Lastly

To finish off the session try to look into your mind's eye, which is just between your eyebrows, and go on a visualisation journey.

Try to think of yourself as being in your favourite place right now. It could be a beach with golden sand and blue sky.

Salute to the Sun – Surya namaskar

This is a beautiful sequence of twelve Asanas carried out slowly and methodically in Hatha Yoga. They can be practised first thing in the morning facing towards the sun, as the name suggests, or in the middle of a yoga session. If time is against you to do a full session, try doing this exhilarating routine and see how wonderful you feel afterwards.

Try to concentrate on breathing while going into and coming out of each pose. You must never feel under any pressure to complete the sequence and always take your time and do the postures you feel you can. Listen to your own body and take careful note of how it feels. There is nothing that should hurt or feel strained and overstretched. If at any point you find anything does hurt or pull, stop, and in your own good time, start again when you're ready. When this set of breathing Asanas is carried out slowly and carefully your body will gain so much benefit from it.

Mountain Pose

1) To begin with, stand in Mountain Pose, with your legs slightly apart.

2) Bring your hands together in prayer position.

3) Inhale.

Backward Bend

4) Lean carefully into the backwards bend and exhale slowly through your mouth, as you say 'ha'.

Mountain Pose

5) Return to the centre again in Mountain Pose.

Forward Bend

6) Exhale slowly through the nose as you go into a Forward Bend.

Lunge

7) Step back with the right leg and into a lunge position. Just breathe normally.

Plank

8) Follow through, stepping back with the left leg, into the Plank position and then inhale.

Upward Facing Dog

9) Exhale as you gently bend your back inwards and look up into the Upward Facing Dog pose.

Downward Facing Dog

10) Inhale next as you slowly bend the opposite way into the Downward Facing Dog pose.

Lunge

11) Exhale as you step forward and follow through to a standing position.

Forward Bend

12) Inhale as you come up from the standing Forward Bend.

Backward Bend

13) Exhale through the mouth as you slightly lean into the Backward Bend.

Mountain Pose

14) Bring your hands back together in prayer pose and finish in Mountain Pose.

≈ 7 ≈

Breathing Exercises-Pranayama

We all breathe automatically without thinking about it because breath is natural for life. Over the past 11 years I have learned various breathing techniques which have enabled me to cope better with day to day life. These ways of controlling the breath or pranayama may also help you relax if practised regularly.

I believe that after warming up and before starting a yoga session, abdominal breathing is essential. This enables everyone to calm their minds and bodies before the session begins. When breathing wanders, the mind is unsteady but when the breath is still, so is the mind. - Hatha Yoga Pradipika.

Before attempting any of the exercises below it is very important to begin gradually observing your breathing. By doing this you will be giving yourself the opportunity to understand it better. Don't worry if you think it is too slow or uneven, what is important is that you are listening to your breath.

Abdominal Breathing:

1) Sit comfortably in either a crossed or straight-legged position on the floor or on a chair.

2) Place the right hand on the abdomen to feel its rise and fall.

3) Put the left hand on the lower rib cage.

4) Inhale deeply and slowly through the nose.

5) Feel the abdomen expand and rise.

6) The chest is kept still while you inhale.

7) Exhale slowly as the abdomen contracts and sinks down.

8) Practice for ten breaths. (1 inhalation and 1 exhalation equal 1 breath).

Benefits:

When you breathe slowly and deeply you bring air into the lower part of the lungs and exercise the diaphragm muscle which can greatly enhance your breathing capacity. This relaxes both the mind and body, calms emotions and massages internal organs and aids sleep.

Full Yogic Breath

1) This is practised exactly the same as above except it brings inhalation into the chest.
2) It is sometimes done with the eyes closed for added comfort.
3) Always do this both slowly and carefully.

Alternate Nostril Breathing-Anuloma Viloma

You probably will not have noticed that when we breathe we breathe mostly through one nostril for an hour or so and then alternate and breathe mostly through the other. Yoga explains this as being two energy channels known as Ida and Pingala, which exist at the nostrils and are constantly changing their dominance. By doing the alternate nostril breathing these two energies are equally balanced.

Please always remember that this breathing exercise must always be undertaken with great care and consideration.

1) Begin using the right hand and placing the middle finger on top of the index finger.

2) Rest these gently between the eyebrows.

3) Close your left nostril with the ring finger.

4) Keep your thumb where it is and inhale slowly to the count of 6.

5) Cover your right nostril with your thumb and, after a few seconds, exhale.

6) After a short rest, inhale slowly to the count of 6 then cover the left nostril with the ring finger and release thumb and exhale through the right nostril, keeping the left nostril closed.

7) These two breaths form one round.

8) Repeat and start with up to 5 rounds.

≈ 8 ≈

Meditation

Meditation has been around since time immemorial and I find it relaxing after a stressful day. Trying to focus the mind on one thing can be a daunting experience at first but, like going to sleep, it is something which comes naturally after a while and I was told that it is good if we can find our own special time and place.

Chris made this place for me to meditate and respects my privacy enough to give me that special time to find myself. He realises the importance of my practice and has helped me all the way. Whenever I go to this room he leaves me in silence for as long as I need and for that I am so grateful.

How I began with Visualisation Journeys

One afternoon while recovering from a relapse, I was lying on the sofa in the lounge. The family was out and I was occupying myself trying to recuperate. As the house was silent I closed my eyes and began to relax and it was completely by accident that I discovered something wonderful. It was a way in which I could help my mind and body work as one. Up until that day I had no idea what it was all about, I unintentionally began thinking of a previous visit I had to a beach abroad. It was a beech in Ibiza we had gone to on a family holiday a few years previously and it was then that I saw beautiful white sand, blue sky and aqua marine sea. I suddenly felt the sun's warmth on my body and a gentle breeze began to caress my skin and I imagined I could hear the waves of the sea crashing against the shore. I unconsciously began to breathe in and out deeply and could even smell the salty sea air. Without me realising it this had an instant and amazing calming effect on my body.

I envisaged myself taking a few steps in the sand towards the sea with the sand feeling warm and soft underfoot with each step I took. I could then see the great ocean in front of me and after walking slowly into the sea, I instantly felt free from my cares and worries. I turned back and returned to where I had come and lay down once again. After opening my eyes and returning to the present I could not describe how I felt inside other than a feeling of utter calm and contentment. I had never felt so connected to that moment before. Nobody had ever told me that my mind could have such a big impact on my body but, without doubt, I realised my mind and body had become connected that day.

That was the first time my mind had taken me on, what can only be described as, a wonderful journey. From that day on I wrote down and monitored the trips I went on and have logged over one hundred such journeys up to now. I always read these to the yoga students at the end of each session as each journey leads to a relaxing and calming end.

The Beach

1) Imagine seeing the perfect beach in your mind's eye, which is just between your eyebrows.

2) See yourself lying on a soft blanket on the sand.

3) Feel the sun's warmth on your skin.

4) There isn't a cloud in the sky and it is so peaceful.

5) Listen to the sound of the sea as the waves gently hit the shore.

6) Nothing can bother you at all here. Relax and enjoy it and let your mind guide you.

≈ 9 ≈

Avenues I have explored

Over the past 11 years I have looked at so many different holistic therapy treatments alongside yoga; reflexology, spa treatments, i.e., sauna, steam room, hydrotherapy pool, fish foot spa, holistic healing and scenar treatment. My search for answers led me to these different treatments which I have written about below. I gained many positive feedbacks from people who have also tried them but realise what suits one person may not suit another. We are all individuals and our bodies respond differently to certain stimuli.

After looking at holistic therapies for physical help, I then sought help with emotional situations. It struck me that my family and friends were very important to me but I did not want to burden them with my MS so, when I visited my doctor, I asked if I could speak to a councillor. My doctor knew I was finding my diagnosis difficult and she agreed. After giving me details of various support groups I was given a number for the MS helpline. I also found so much support from my neurologist and MS nurse.

Reflexology:

According to the Association of Reflexologists; reflexology is a non-intrusive complementary therapy based on the theory that different points on the feet, lower leg, hands, face or ears correspond with different areas of the body. The treatment is to promote better health within the client and I, as the client, felt amazing afterwards.

Spa Treatments:

I have been on various spa break treatments after a relapse and have always returned feeling much better. The steam room I always found suited me, as it helped me to breathe much better and the hydrotherapy pool was very effective on the muscles.

Fish Foot Spa:

I had my first treatment in Sheffield when visiting Michelle at university. What a wonderful experience we had and I enjoyed it so much that I went for a second treatment in Durham whilst visiting Dominic. It was at the Bon Appe Feet where I was made coffee and people chatted to me quite happily. The treatments were absolutely lovely for warming my feet and making me feel very happy afterwards. I personally recommend this treatment.

Holistic Healing:

This gave me a wonderful relaxed feeling and it also complimented yoga. I slept so soundly and awoke in the morning feeling mentally alert. My mind was very sharp and it is definitely something worth trying and very enjoyable. I did feel a very strong sensation running down my legs during the treatment which was quite extraordinary.

Scenar Treatment:

This natural treatment was recommended to me by a friend after a relapse. According to the Scenar website, the Russian scientists and doctors developed this treatment in the late 1970s for the Russian space programme. It is a small portable device weighing no more than 30 grams and is energy efficient, multi-applicable and non-invasive. Treatment involves a painless procedure which sends electrical signals to stimulate the immune system and I can say it seems to work well alongside yoga. It is definitely a 21st century treatment and I highly recommend it to my family and friends.

Family and Friends Support:

I am so glad that I have a supportive family and wonderful group of friends. Chris has been my rock throughout my years of living with MS. He knows so much about it through me and when we married he accepted it as being a part of me and we learned to pull together through tough times. Michelle and Dominic have always been there for me and I too for them. They have picked me up from falls, seen me after relapses and driven me to many places when needed. They saw a lot while growing up and are two caring, young adults. If I needed shopping they were there. My friends like Tina, Tammy and both Claire's have been so good to me. Tammy would collect my prescriptions when needed and both Claire's would offer me a shoulder and a cuppa. After my last relapse the three of us went to a spa day together and had a wonderful therapeutic time. Tina would always be around to offer her support and friendship. They would all make me feel more sociable and this was the treatment I needed. Friends and family are antidotes in themselves.

Counselling:

This really did help me to deal with the news I had MS. I felt less angry and dealt with the diagnosis much better. It was as though I had lost sight of myself and forgotten who I was as a person. I realise now that it felt as though I was grieving for the loss of my old self. It was a scary feeling at first not knowing how this was going to affect my life. At the onset of MS it was a lonely time and talking to someone who didn't judge me really helped and talking helped me to accept myself for who I am.

Support Groups:

I have found the support I received from the Ryedale branch to be excellent. Day trips were planned and I was always invited along. One of the most helpful people was my support officer who was always a very approachable, caring person. If I needed advice about anything at all she was, and still is, the one person I contact. The volunteers in the MS shop are such strong, passionate people and most of them also have MS. After meeting and having the pleasure of working alongside these girls, I realise they are really strong.
The Buddies group is a place where people of all ages with MS meet up once a month and chat and get to know each other. I have been going to this group in Scarborough now for a few years and find it very relaxing to be amongst people who understand each other.

MS Helpline:

This free helpline number has been available to all MS patients in the U.K. for as long as I can remember. They have offered help in different areas of my life and are caring, friendly and helpful. Whenever I needed to talk they always had a listening ear. They know MS symptoms are different for every one of us and they suggest different treatments to help.

Neurologist and MS Nurse:

From the very start of my diagnosis the neurologist has been there. He helped me from the outset and is so knowledgeable about the condition and advised me to have specific treatments at the right times. Although my MS nurse is based in James Cook Hospital, she is always at the other end of the telephone. I have a direct line to her and her support has been invaluable.

Beta-Interferon Injections: Otherwise known as Interferon Beta1a and 1b

There are various types of this injection and different ways to administer it. I use Avonex beta-1a, 0.5mls. According to the MS website, it is a protein that is naturally found in the human body and helps fight viral infections in the immune system. Clinical trials have shown the relapse rate to be reduced by around a third in two years. It seems to act as a defence against the disease. I cannot stop its progression but I can help to slow it down. Yoga keeps my leg muscles strong, so I invariably feel less pain.

Gabapentin:

I have been prescribed these 300mg drugs by my neurologist. According to the NHS website these drugs are used to treat peripheral neuropathic pain. I found them helpful with the pain of optical neuritis.

Sunshine/ Vitamin D:

I must admit this has always been one of the most beneficial factors for me. I know vitamin D has been in the media headlines recently, stating how good it is for people with MS. I have taken yoga with me to places like Ibiza, Majorca and Fuerta Ventura and gained so much pleasure from the sunshine. There are several other people like myself who seem to feel a whole lot happier while feeling the sun's warmth.

Healthy Eating:

This has always been an important factor to most people with or without MS. I believe that you are what you eat. I always say that I eat to live but don't live to eat. I prefer to eat small meals often but everyone has their own routine. I believe always in soups but sometimes it is alright to meet friends for a curry and an eighties night.

Vitamins:

I have been trying to keep my immune system strong by taking certain vitamins and I now believe it may help me support my system and help reduce my chances of infection. I always take the vitamins my doctor prescribes me; Calcichew with D3. I bought Omega 3 over the counter because I believe it helps the brain and nervous system. I take a low dose of Cranberry because it seems to help control water infections and vitamin B complex because it helps the nervous system.

End Conclusion

I still wonder what the cause of MS is; could it have been awoken by my bicycle accident? Was it lying dormant or could the chemicals leaking through the air vents at the factory have poisoned me? I wonder sometimes if the main instigator was when I contracted salmonella whilst abroad. Whatever the cause of the disease I have always believed a cure will be found in the near future. I realise now that the cause is, in fact, not as important as the cure.

There are so many clinical trials going on at the moment which I find very encouraging. I believe that a cure may come from stem cell surgery, mainly because I have heard such good results through the media lately.

Meanwhile, I will keep on doing my own research into the disease as well as browsing through the MS Society web site. The MS newsletter is so informative and helps to keep everyone up to date with news of possible cures and on-going treatments. My hope is that, in time, MS will be understood by many more people across the world.

I am not teaching at the moment because I have spent some time writing this book and I hope it will help as many people as possible find peace and calm in a stressful world. The yoga tool I have been given might also be useful to you at some point in your life whether you have MS or not or know someone who has the disease. I hope you gain some benefit from this book.

Before undertaking these exercises, please, firstly consult your G.P. where necessary.

Maria Hawkes

Diplomas in:

British School Of Yoga
Yoga Class Instructing
Advanced Hatha Yoga Teacher
Anatomy and Physiology